SO-AHQ-582

Contents

Part One – Early Detectors
Early Detectors 5
Integrating Detector 12
Crystal Detector 13
The Audion 16
Armstrong Regenerative Detector............................ 18
Ultra-Audion Circuit 20
Simplicity and Performance 22
Too Much Positive Feedback Creates Oscillation 26
Regeneration in the Receiver 27
The Receiver Becomes a Transmitter 28
Detector Sensitivity 29

Part Two – Regenerative Detection
Three Machines in One 33
Grid Leak Detector 34
Detection of CW Signals 40
Sum and Difference 43
Heterodyning in Practice 44

Part Three – Challenges of Regenerative Receiver Design
Electrical and Mechanical Stability Imperative 47
Ways to Control Regeneration 48
Quality Capacitors Needed 50
Modifying AM Broadcast Variable Capacitors 51
Choke Keeps RF Out of Audio Circuit 54
Potentiometer Control of Regeneration 55
Control of Screen Voltages 57
Two Bypass Capacitors Recommended 57
Lower Frequencies Recommended for Beginners 58
Coil Problems 59
Rules for Numbers of Turns 61

Part Four – Building a Practical Regenerative Receiver
Wire Size for Coils 64
Plug-In Coil Forms 65
Designing the Coils 68

Wind the Coils 71
Antenna May Cause Dead Spots 73
Hand Capacity Causes Instability 75
Phones or Speaker? 76
Field Effect Transistors in Place of Vacuum Tubes 78
Build the Receiver Like a Battleship 81
Slow-Motion Vernier Dial Drive Essential 82
Solid State Doerle Receiver 86
Separate Regeneration FET Receiver 89
Why JFETS over Bipolars? 92
Superregeneration 92
Proper Regenerative Operation 93
Fringe Howl 96
Eliminating Fringe Howl 98
Double Twin-Triode Receiver 99
Pentode-Triode Receiver 102
The Double Regenerative Superhet 105
Tube Pin Connections 108
Older Books Hold Secrets 109

Part Five – Sample Regenerative Receiver Circuits

.... 111

Appendix

.... 121

Dedicated to my grandsons, Jon and William.

C. F. "Rock" Rockey

Part One

Early Detectors

In radio, just what is detection anyway? No radio detector "detects" anything, be it re-generative or otherwise. What it does is to make the information content of a radio signal available to a human mind – or at least, it is the most essential step in such a process. Probably the choice of the word "detection" was unfortunate. But since it has been with us for so long we are loath to abandon it out of respect for radio's interesting past.

Early Detectors

The earliest "wireless" detectors were crude and unreliable devices. By today's standards these were most insensitive. In the light of modern experience one wonders how some of them could have worked at all! Dr. Heinrich Hertz, the true father of radio in the writer's opinion, was the first human to intentionally set-up electromagnetic waves (of greater wave length than infra-red, or "heat" rays) in free-space and study their properties. He generated these waves with its simple, spark-coil-excited "Hertzian Dipole" and detected them with a very closely-spaced spark-gap in his little receiving loop "resonator". Where the waves were strong, the resonator gap sparked brilliantly. Otherwise the spark was weak or nonexistent.

In Guglielmo Marconi's time, during the "gay nineties" of the 19th Century, "wireless" detectors were usually equivalent to carefully set-up loose-connections, often called "Coherers." Marconi's favorite, which he used com-

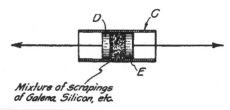

Figure 1.1 – Cross Section of a Marconi Coherer

mercially for a number of years, consisted of a little glass tube about two inches long and one-third inch in diameter (Fig 1.1). There was a metallic plug at each end and the space between was loosely packed with a fine mixture of nickel and silver filings (and some other "secret-stuff" which Marconi didn't reveal). Normally, this pile of particles was electrically non-conductive, that is, an open-circuit. A battery, a sensitive relay and a then-common telegraph sounder were connected in series with the coherer along with an antenna (which Marconi may really have invented) and ground.

In the absence of a received signal, the circuit was thus open and dead. But when a signal arrived, its impulsive, highly damped voltage somehow stimulated the filings to stick together (or cohere), thus closing the battery

> *A common way of ascertaining the sensitiveness of a coherer or detector is to operate a small electric bell or buzzer in its vicinity with one or two dry cells. For instance, in the case of the De Forest responder, which is freely exposed extraneous waves, as shown in Fig. 86, the adjustment of the instrument may be regulated by the waves set up by such a bell or buzzer, the distance of the bell from the antenna giving a clue to the sensitiveness of the adjustment. A filings-coherer for operating at a distance of about twelve miles should be sensitive to such a bell at a distance of at least six feet. A very sensitive coherer will be affected by the oscillations thus set up at a distance of forty or fifty feet and with doors and walls intervening.*

—from Maver's Wireless Telegraphy (circa World War I)

circuit and announcing the wave's appearance via the sounder. But, like some people who cannot shut-up when they have nothing more worthwhile to say, the recalcitrant pile of fillings failed to separate after the wave had passed. The device was thus rendered deaf after the first hit of the signal. To correct this unhappy condition, Marconi connected the hammer mechanism from an electric doorbell in the relay circuit. When a wave came along, this little "electrical hammer" gave the coherer a sharp smack! This de-cohered the filings and prepared the circuit for the next set of waves. Believe it or not, this detecting arrangement proved commercially useful for some time, called forth lifesaving assistance in several serious marine disasters, and otherwise demonstrated the practical valve of wireless.

7

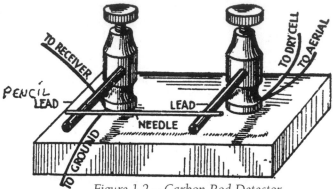

Figure 1.2 – Carbon Rod Detector

Other similar gimmicks were also used as detectors. One, often used by early radio amateurs, consisted of a pair of small carbon rods (probably liberated from used flashlight batteries) arranged mutually parallel and bridged by an ordinary steel sewing needle (Fig 1.2). This contraption was connected in series with a single dry cell and, when available, a pair of headphones. Otherwise an ordinary, hand-held telephone receiver, sometimes stolen from a local pay telephone booth, was used. The antenna was connected to one of the rods, the ground connection to the other. Since there were so few signals on the air at the time, often no one bothered to provide any means for tuning. When a strong enough signal did appear, it somehow caused the electrical resistance of the carbon steel junction to be increased as long as the signal was present.

Wireless signals of the time consisted of a series of wave trains – one "train" for each spark that jumped the transmitter's spark gap. The receiving phones reproduced the buzzing of the transmitter's spark coil in the young operator's ear. Called an "auto-coherer" because, unlike Marconi's filing-tube, it did not need to be smacked, it decohered itself. This set-up served widely until the electrolytic-detector appeared several years thereafter.

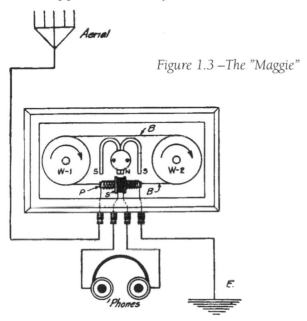

Figure 1.3 – The "Maggie"

Because these cohering contraptions were so often a pain in his operators' necks, particularly aboard a ship in a storm, Marconi and his experts devised their famous magnetic detector, often called the "Maggie" (Fig 1.3). This was not much more sensitive to weak signals than a coherer but it was definitely more reliable. It consisted of a flexible continuous band of iron wires passing continuously around a pair of pulleys. When the pulleys were rotated by a spring powered motor, the iron band was

9

continuously pulled past a pair of horse shoe magnets which kept it magnetized. At another point the moving band passed through a pair of concentric coils, one being connected through a tuner (interference having increasing during the intervening years) to the antenna system, the other to a pair of headphones. When an alternating current signal energized the antenna coil, it temporarily disturbed the magnetism in the moving iron band. This magnetic disturbance induced a voltage into the headphone coil and produced a sound into the operator's ear. The whole device, except for the tuning coils and the headphones, of course, was built into a neat wooden box which somewhat resembled a reel-to-reel tape recorder.

The "Maggie" normally required little adjustment. It continued to respond to incoming signals for as long as an hour before the spring motor requiring winding. Through inattention or fatigue, an operator might forget to wind it, and then the receiver went dead. At sea, this could have tragic consequences. Stories are still told of a number of ships being located within ready assistance range of the ill-fated *Titanic*. Tired operators, snoozing, with heads lying upon radio room tables, allowed their "Maggies" to run down thus missing the *Titanic's* urgent SOS calls. These operators, and their ship's captains were unaware of the tragedy unfolding. So many lives were unnecessarily lost.

But perhaps the strangest detecting instrument with which this writer is acquainted was a frog's leg (freshly removed from a frog, naturally) and a kinegraph which was essentially an oscillograph, on which a stylus could scratch a trace into smoked paper attached to a slowly revolving drum. When connected to an antenna, the frog's leg was sensitive to electrical signals to the degree that signals could be read from the smoked paper! Signals were recorded from the Eiffel Tower transmitter at several hundred kilometers distance! Where but in France would such an imaginative experiment have been done? A good textbook published before World War One will probably describe the many other seemingly "wild and woolly" methods for extracting information from radio signals. You may find these as interesting as I have.

However, all of the detecting means described here thus far, suffered from a most serious defect; they were not integrating devices. That is, they responded only to impulses, in other words, to the sharp rise of the incoming signal voltage; they did not accumulate the signal energy and thus produce the greatest response. Most of them would have utterly failed to reproduce radio telephone signals or pure continuous wave, also known as CW or radio-telegraphy, both of which remain in use today.

Integrating Detector

Perhaps the first integrating detector to be developed was the electrolytic detector, now attributed to professor Reginald Fessenden, about 1905 (Fig 1.4). It consisted of a small cup of dilute nitric acid into which was dipped an extremely fine strand of platinum wire such as the Wollaston Wire, an unworkably fine

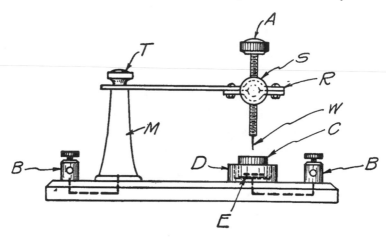

Figure 1.4 – Integrating Detector

platinum wire which was coated with a thick layer of silver. For use in this detector the silver layer was dissolved off in strong nitric acid, leaving only the platinum wire, "as fine as frog hair," in the cup of acid. In use, the wire was connected through the tuning coil and head phones to a single dry cell whose biasing voltage, a critical quantity, was adjusted by a potentiometer. When the biasing voltage was set properly and the length of wire exposed to the acid was correct, the electrolytic detector was universally regarded as the most sensitive wireless detector developed to that date. This was the detector used by Dr. L. W. Austin when he made one of the first true long distance radio wave propagation tests for the United States Navy in 1910. Transmission to and from naval ships were made at varying distances up to 1850 nautical miles, the received signals strength being then measured carefully at many points. From these measurements, curves were drawn and equations derived which were used in radio engineering until well after World War One. An inkling of the true potential of long distance wave propagation was gained. It wasn't until the 1920's that the short waves were opened up, and propagation was studied thoroughly.

Although it was a truly sensitive detector, this open cup form of the electrolytic detector was unwieldy in many situations. Who wants an open cup of nitric acid setting around? In response, Hugo Gernsback invented a totally enclosed form, with a spill-proof container of acid. He called it the "Radioson." He sold many of these to radio amateurs round about World War One it is said.

Crystal Detector

During this same period of intense radio development, between 1905 and 1915, the notorious crystal detector was discovered and

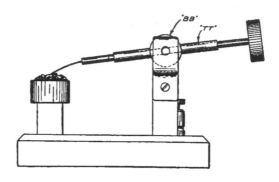

Figure 1.5 – Galena Crystal Detector

modified by a number of inventors(Fig 1.5). This popular gadget with its galena cryrstal and cat's whisker is familiar to anyone who has ever built or used a crystal set. But galena is not the only mineral that can be used. Almost every electrically conductive crystalline substance from gold ore to anthracite coal was tested for its detecting properties. A modified form that used two different crystals which touched one another but used no cat-whisker wire was tried and generated a sizeable patent fight in the court system.

After much experimenting and fooling around, the cat whisker form was finally settled upon, using a galena, iron pyrite or silicon crystal, as the most practical. Which crystal is best? Well, as the circus barker says; "You pays your money and takes your choice..." Laugh as you may, until the advent of the triode vacuum tube, the crystal detector was the world standard detector particularly for shipboard service. When the cat-whisker was carefully adjusted and touched a particularly sensitive spot on the crystal, it was nearly as sensitive as an electrolytic detector. Furthermore, it is cheap, simple and effective as thousands of people discovered when AM radio broadcasting began, and people began to build their own receivers.

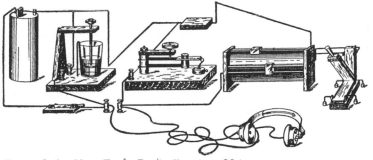

Figure 1.6 – Very Early Radio Receiver Using
an Acid Integrating Detector

Why were the electrolytic and crystal detectors so much more sensitive and so much more useful than their predecessors? First, because these are integrating detectors. They permit the incoming signal waves to build up within the circuit during the whole time of a dit or a dah, rather than responding to instantaneous changes in signal strength and ignoring the energy that follows. Secondly, they are rectifying devices, that is, when supplied with a source of alternating voltage such as a received radio signal, they allow current to flow much more readily in one direction than in the other. This not only preserves the quality of a complex received signal much more completely, but also reproduces amplitude modulated radio telephone signals with much less

15

distortion. Indeed most of today's vacuum tube and solid state detectors are of the rectifying sort – in one way or another. And many are used. . .

The Audion

For many reasons one may say that the modern age of radio began with the invention of Dr. Lee deForest's three element vacuum tube the Audion about 1906. True, a vacuum two element rectifying valve had preceded it, but as a detector, all this could do way rectify the signal, and a crystal did that nearly as well and in a way that was simpler and cheaper and less susceptible to breakage. The three element audion tube was the very first signal amplifying device which worked at all well at high radio frequencies as well as at lower audio frequencies. But the story of the vacuum tube's development is a fascinating one which can be but touched upon here.

The first Audions were frail, short-lived, and inconsistent devices. Until he could financially arrange to manufacture them himself, Dr. deForest had them made for him in a light bulb factory. Light bulbs in that day were not the reliable, bright lamps that know today. Both light bulb and Audion filaments burned out much too soon because the manufacturer could not suck out enough air out of the glass bulb to achieve the necessary degree of vacuum. Frequently, even this poor vacuum was soon lost when the gas absorbed within the internal metal elements was released as the tube was used. No two of Doc deForest's early Audion tubes were electrically alike. You had to experiment with plate and filament voltages until the darn thing worked as it should. Sometimes it never would work properly, burning out before you could get it adjusted!

Since they were not mass produced, these tubes were very expensive! An ordinary working man might have to work for several months to pay for a new one. Use too much filament voltage and that little glowing wire soon parted. Use too much plate or, as they called it, wing voltage and the tube got a blue glow inside. If this condition were allowed to continue the vacuum would be ruined! You had to mind your Ps-and-Qs when you used one of Doc deForest's early fire bottles! But, oh boy, when you did get the crazy thing set up right, how those signals rolled in! Even a weak, little spark coil transmitter could be heard for fifteen or twenty miles. Before the Audion days, it might have covered five miles, with a struggle! A large amateur kilowatt spark rig could now work five hundred miles at night and on cold winter nights, could often cover a thousand! The vacuum tube made long distance amateur communication a practical reality.

In the issues of the amateur radio magazine, *QST*, for the year 1916, you can read of how personal "telegram" messages were passed from coast to coast by amateurs in four or five hundred mile hops. This feat was repeated several times in following years. It would not have been possible had not the participating amateur radio telegraphers used Audions in their receivers.

There is not enough time or space to relate the vital role that tubes played in the First World War. Suffice it to say that vacuum tube technology was advanced to the point that by 1921, tubes had taken on a recognizable modern appearance. Their basic design changed little until the advent of the screen grid tubes, pentodes, and even the "iron tubes" in the early thirties.

Armstrong Regenerative Detector

Aside from the invention and development of the vacuum tube perhaps the greatest advance in the detector art itself was made in 1912 when Edwin Armstrong conceived the idea of coupling the plate or output circuit of a vacuum tube detector back into the input or grid circuit (Fig 1.7). His idea then was that any signal fed into the grid circuit would be amplified four or five times by a tube of that era upon the first trip through. Then some of it would pass around the feedback connection and be amplified again to increase its strength by twenty-five times. On the third pass it would again be amplified some 125 times and on the fourth pass 625 times, for instance.

He tried this first by tuning the plate as well as the grid circuit to the signal frequency and by Jimminy it worked. Later he found that instead of tuning both the grid and plate circuits to the signal frequency, it was generally more convenient to wind a little coil, later

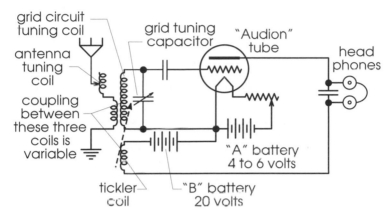

Figure 1.7 – Edwin Armstrong's best Audion circuit

called the tickler coil, and connect it into the plate circuit. This tickler coil could be magnetically coupled to the grid circuit. If one mounted this little coil upon a rotating shaft connected to a dial upon the receiver's front panel, both the amount of energy fed back and its relative phase, or direction of action, could be easily controlled. By so doing, it was found that the total amplification developed by one tube could amount to thousands of times.

If both the magnitude and phase of the signal fed back were very carefully adjusted, this feed back voltage can aid rather than oppose, the signal voltage already present in the

19

input circuit. On the other hand, were the voltage fed back in such a way as to oppose the input voltage, the total circuit amplification could be drastically reduced, theoretically down to zero. Today, we refer to these conditions as positive feedback and negative feedback respectively. These concepts have been found to be very useful in other spheres of technology, such as in high quality music amplification, in automatic industrial process control, even by mechanical analogy to the design of automobile suspension and braking systems. While positive feedback insures increased amplification, negative feedback provides greater system stability (at the expense of lower circuit gain, of course).

In Figure 1.7 we see Edwin Armstrong's best circuit as it would appear in modern form.

Old timers will immediately notice how closely later regenerative circuits resemble this early circuit. This is, of course, no accident.

Ultra-Audion Circuit

Dr. Lee deForest had been experimenting with a feedback circuit at about the same time as Armstrong and had developed a circuit which also worked quite well. He named it the Ultra-Audion circuit (Fig 1.8). Here, signal voltage was also fed back from output to input circuit but the feedback path was not quite so obvious.

In Figure 1.8 we see the grid and plate of

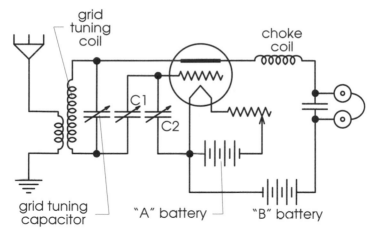

Figure 1.8 – Lee deForest's "Ultra-Audion" circuit

the Audion are connected to opposite ends of
the tuned circuit, thus insuring that the phase
relation of the input and output voltages are
correct for positive feedback. But the magnitude of the feedback voltage is controlled by
the ratio of the capacitances of C1 and C2.
For proper operation C1 should be a larger
capacitor than C2, usually. The choke coil is a
coil of relatively many turns, many more than
those upon the grid tuning coil, for instance.
Its job is to prevent RF currents from being
short circuited from the plate to the filament
through the phone bypass capacitor and the B
battery.

While this circuit did work satisfactorily,
and became quite popular with the US Navy,
it is much trickier to handle that Armstrong's
circuit. By now, you probably realize that the
term regeneration when applied to circuits

such as the two just described, refers the application of controlled positive feedback to increase the signal amplification of the circuit. Both Armstrong and deForest had patent claims to this process, and were bitterly opposed to each other. It was said that each claimed to have the valid patent for it, and almost came to blows, once, at an Institute of Radio Engineers meeting in New York. But those were tough times! Everyone was infringing someone else's patent and legally trying to defend his own. Court battles were prolonged and bitter. (And as might be expected, the lawyers made the most money thereby).

These two were not the only two regenerative circuits around back then by any means. It seemed that everyone active in the field devised his own circuit and made big claims for its performance. However, when the involved schematic diagrams were unscrambled, many were found to be the same, at least in principle. Some turned out to be easier to use in practice, others more stable in operation or cheaper to build. But, when the chips were down, when properly used, all would perform equally well.

Simplicity and Performance

The most important things to understand is that a properly built and used regenerative detector can have a practical signal voltage amplification of some ten thousand times though using but one tube! We will see that we can say the same for one transistor also. This is about as much amplification as would be achieved by two or three typical modern triode tubes connected in cascade, or following each other, in an amplification chain. Think of the number of parts this might save, for instance!

On the other hand, it remains true that the improvements in gain have their costs. Positive feedback, or regeneration, always brings with it a proportional decrease in operating stability. To realize such amplification, as we mention here, requires that the circuit must be adjusted near to a narrow peak upon its operating curve, and this is a tricky condition to maintain. It demands care and attention by the user.

Now that we have spoken generally about the effect of regeneration upon circuit behavior, let's toss around a few numbers and see what turns up. More recently, some years after Armstrong's and deForest's times we have a more thorough study of the behavior of feedback circuits in a numerical way.

In schematic shown in Figure 1.9, block A represents an amplifier along with its power supply and other necessary parts, and B represents a feedback coupling network such as magnetically coupled coils, capacitor coupling or any other network arranged to couple some of the output voltage back into the input circuit. The input voltage, supplied by the AC

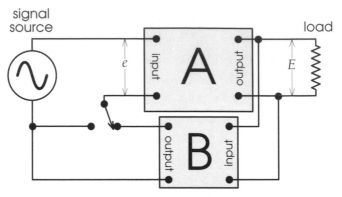

Figure 1.9 – Block Diagram of a Regenerative Feedback Circuit

generator, the signal source, is represented by the voltage e, while E represents the amplifier output voltage. When the circuit is in operation, and the switch is thrown to the left, the only input to the amplifier is that provided by the signal source. But when the switch is thrown to the right, some of the output voltage is fed back into the input circuit. The ratio of the voltage feedback to the output voltage, the "feedback ratio" is represented in the formula by the symbol, B. The amplification of the system with no feedback at all, only the bare amplifier being used, is

$$\frac{\text{Output}}{\text{Input}} = \frac{E}{e} = A$$

The voltage being feed back from the output, compared to the output voltage itself is

$$\frac{e}{E} = \frac{\text{Feedback}}{\text{Output}} = B$$

or the feedback ratio. Since we are operating

this system in the positive feedback or regenerative condition, we may find the amplification with feedback by using the formula:

$$A_F = \frac{A}{(1-AB)}$$

Where A_F now represents the amplification when the system is regenerative, and A, that of the "bare" amplification of the tube or transistor. Picking a system in which the bare amplification is ten times, let us tabulate the regenerative amplification possible–

Feedback Ratio (B)	Working Regenerative Amplification, A_F	
.00	10	
0.01	11	
0.03	14.2	
0.05	20	
0.07	33	*Figure 1.10 –*
0.08	50	*Increasing Positive*
0.09	100	*Feedback in the*
0.095	200	*Regenerative Receiver*
0.099	1000	*Increases Gain*
0.0999	10,000	Critical Feedback
		—Lies About Here
.01	infinity	

There is scarcely a better recommendation for regeneration than is provided by this table! Note, that as more and more voltage is fed back in the positive direction, the greater the amplification produced by a tube without changing its DC voltages. However, this process cannot be extended indefinitely. After all, there is no free lunch, 'tis said.

Too Much Positive Feedback Creates Oscillation

If we play with the feedback formula we find that as we plug larger and larger feedback ratio numbers into the formula we finally reach the point where the denominator of the fraction reaches zero. That is, as B increases, the denominator, (1-AB), gets smaller and smaller. If the term, AB, ever equals one, the denominator will be zero. Dividing by zero is forbidden in mathematics!

Dividing any number by an extremely small number results in an extremely large quotient. In the extreme case where the denominator approaches zero, the result approaches infinity or ∞. Infinity is an incalculably large result, indeed it has no real meaning in practical life. So, when this happens, we know that an unusual condition has developed which the math can no longer help us, as it were.

If we actually build such a circuit with excessive feedback, we find out what happens and what ∞ really means in the real world. Yep, as we radio people put it, the circuit goes into oscillation. What does this mean? In plain talk we say that the circuit is now receiving all of its input signal from its own output around through the feedback path! With the circuit in oscillation we may remove the external signal source entirely, and the output signal will remain virtually unchanged!

Regeneration in the Receiver

If you have had experience with a regenerative receiver, you can easily follow in your mind what is happening here. With phones on the head, turn up the regeneration control whatever it might be: rotating tickler coil, variable capacitor, variable resistor, etc. You will observe that the hissing noise you hear, due to the vibration of the atoms in the circuit parts, this noise will increase until it reaches a maximum. At this point the circuit feedback is very close to its critical point. If you turn the control up just a bit more, and if your receiver is a good one, you will hear a strange noise that is best described as "swish" or "tunk". This is the point where in the feedback is just over the critical value, and the detector is oscillating. Thus you, yourself, have confirmed just what our formula, and our table, is telling you in mathematical form. If you increase the regeneration control further, you will observe that the circuit noise does not get any stronger. In fact it gets weaker.

If you increase the regeneration control further, you will observe that the circuit noise does not get any stronger. In fact, it gets weaker still, telling you that the circuit can develop no more amplification than that obtained at the critical feedback value. That it actually becomes less is due to properties of the tube or transistor in use and is caused by internal conditions therein.

If you will think about this for a moment, I believe that you will agree that the invention of the regenerative detector was one of the greatest events in the history of radio. Because the amplification obtained by the use of positive feedback is so remarkably large, the regenerative detector is, in itself, the most sensitive detector ever discovered!

The Receiver Becomes a Transmitter

In addition, its invention uncovered not only a remarkable receiving device, but also a most marvelous radio signal source! Take a moment to imagine a simple electronic device either vacuum tube or solid state that will generate an alternating current that is as pure or even more pure in some cases, than that which the finest rotating alternator can produce. And this circuit can produce this AC current at any frequency from a few Hertz to hundreds of megaHertz! No mechanical device can do this. While our emphasis in this discussion is on receiving using a near-oscillating detector producing only milliwatts of AC power, larger tubes, and some semiconductors, have been developed which, using the same principle as used in an oscillating detector, can produce hundreds or thousands of watts if needed! Or, more practically, the high frequency A.C. signal output of a small oscillating tube or transistor is readily amplified through a cascade of increasingly larger amplifiers until megawatts are obtained! This is common in short wave broadcast transmitters, for example. Thus, the invention of the electronic oscillator has eliminated the noisy, stinking, buzzy old spark-gap transmitters that ate up hundreds of kiloHertz with their broadbanded signals. Gone are the huge, hissing arc transmitters which were useful only at the longest wavelengths, drank up pure alcohol by the gallon, and spewed spurious signals all over the spectrum back in the "good" old days! Today we use only continuous waves for communication, and these are generated by electronic oscillators. It is the use of these continuous waves, having an original single frequency which, after suitable modulation, made radiotelephony practical, and, later, television. No spark or arc transmitter could have been used practically for these.

Detector Sensitivity

We can create a table (Fig. 1.11) which shows the minimum amount of power that is detectable by each type of detector. It is generally agreed that the great gain in modern transmission distance range has been obtained

Detector Type	Minimum Signal Strength (watts)
Filings Coherer (Marconi Type)	4×10^{-8}
Carbon Steel Coherer Auto-Coherer	2×10^{-9}
Magnetic Detector "Maggie"	10^{-9}
Electrolytic Detector	7×10^{-11}
Carborundum Crystal	9×10^{-10}
Non-Regenerative "Audion"	3×10^{-12}
Regenerative "Audion"	10^{-12}
Modern Regenerative	10^{-15} or better

Figure 1.11 – Relative Sensitivity of Various Detectors

more through the increase of receiving sensitivity than by increase in transmitter power.

Although effective distance range depends strongly upon signal path and the frequency of operation, the type of antennas used at each end of the path, the transmission conditions at the time and the skill of the operators, we do now know the importance of detector sensitivity in practical radio cannot be denied. Based upon the writer's experience, short wave Morse code signals from very low powered amateur stations in Asia, Australia and New

Zealand are regularly heard with a simple regenerative receiver here in the USA.

We may safely say that the invention and
use of regeneration both as a detector and as
an oscillator are what have made long range
radio communication a daily occurrence. And,
it should be noted, such feats had been ac-
complished long before modern sophisticated
receivers and automatic modes of transmission were available.

Although the present trend in radio tends
toward a longing for the ever more sophisticated and complex communication apparatus,
there remains a significant group of individuals who continue to thrive on simplicity. These
same individuals neither have, nor desire to
spend, the money required to follow the state
of the radio art. In any case, there remains a
sizeable group which enjoy the construction
and operation of simple, regenerative receivers, usually for the shortwave frequencies.
Others among us find delight in making use
therein of discarded or obsolete components,
often salvaged from the junk pile. A regenerative receiver can provide a thought-provok-
ing challenge to one trying to recycle junk radio parts. In order to stimulate this construc-
tion-oriented subset of our receiver building
population, of which I am a proud member,
let us discuss some of the theory and application of the modern, relatively simple, but effective short wave regenerative receiver. These
days there is a paucity of material published

in this field. Is it too old-fashioned? Let our exploration here be, at least, a partial remedy for this condition. Building a regenerative receiver is both educational and fun, as well as inexpensive. It will stimulate both your imagination and your skill.

RADIO · TV · ELECTRONICS

For short-wave listening away from home, or to check on your own "set," build this

Portable Short-Wave Receiver

BY C. F. ROCKEY, W9SCH

Portable receiver brings in short-wave signals from a surprising distance. Vernier tuning dial helps to separate stations.

ment voltage to the single tube (Fig. 3). Simple mounting of the batteries speeds replacement when they are exhausted. Since this bottom shelf is narrower than the box, the copper contact strips will not short out against the sides. Screws through from the outside hold the shelves in position inside the box.

The upper or socket shelf supports the tube, coil and most of the wiring. Screws (#6 x ½-in. rh) through the sides of the box into the wood of the shelf support this one, too. To locate the shelf, place the "B" battery in position and set the shelf firmly on it so it wedges the battery in place. Unscrew the shelf and complete the wiring according to the pictorial and schematic

SIGNAL pick-up from transmitters several hundred miles away are normal with this 1-tube, inexpensive receiver that's battery powered and simple to build into a tackle box. I have picked up ships sailing off the coast of South America while fishing in the Wisconsin woods, using only a 20-ft impromptu antenna.

Back in the mid-1950's, C. F. Rockey wrote numerous articles for Science and Mechanics Magazine and Radio-TV Experimenter. Here we see an article from April 1954 describing construction of a single-tube regenerative receiver.

than the usual metal chassis.

Locating the wood shelves in the box is a good point to start construction. My shelves were ¾ x 2⅝ x 5 in., but you may need to change dimensions to fit the utility box you plan to use. The 22½-volt "B" battery is wedged in place on the bottom shelf and copper contact strips hold the flashlight cells that provide "A" battery or fila-

Two wood shelves separate radio components from batteries and simplify construction and wiring.

Part Two

Regenerative Detection

Three Machines in One

Although not generally realized, a regenerative detector is truly a triple threat device. It is a rectifying detector, a positive feedback amplifier and, for CW code reception, a heterodyne oscillator – all in one envelope! While it is becoming common to use the more readily available field effect transistor as a regenerative detector, it may be easier to understand circuit operation when a triode vacuum tube is used. So let's consider this device first.

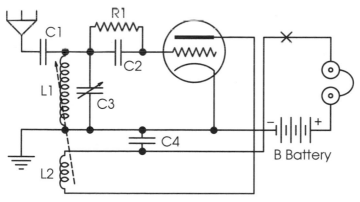

Figure 2.1 – Basic Regenerative Receiver

Remember that the circuit shown in Figure 2.1 is just the bare bones circuit. Such vital details as careful control of the degree of feedback, a radio frequency choke coil at point "X", possibly an audio frequency amplifier instead of the head phones, a means to heat the tubes cathode, and perhaps other details have been either been assumed or have been omitted in this simplification.

Any available medium-mu triode (see appendix) may be used. C1 is a small antenna coupling capacitor of possibly five picofarads. C2 is, universally called the grid capacitor and is usually 50 or 100 pfd. C4 is the plate bypass capacitor, of about 1000 pfd. R1 is the grid leak resistor of several megohms value. The B battery is often replaced by a line powered power supply circuit. We will try to adhere to these conventions, making changes only when necessary.

Grid Leak Detector

There are a number of ways to operate a simple triode vacuum tube, each of which will make it act as a detector. However, in this discussion, we will consider that arrangement which has been found to be most sensitive to the weak signals which are of greatest interest in shortwave reception. This particular circuit arrangement is usually called a grid leak detector. If for the moment we disregard the feedback circuitry needed for regeneration, the schematic diagram might look like that in Figure 2.2.

In operation, an electromagnetic wave of particular frequency induces a voltage in the antenna. Assuming that the tuning compo-

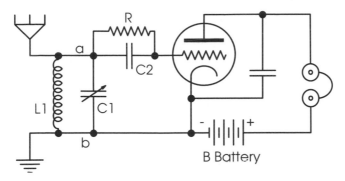

Figure 2.2 – Basic Grid Leak Detector

nents, L and C, are adjusted to the wave's frequency, the wave develops an alternating voltage across points a and b. This voltage then acts through capacitor C2 on the grid of the tube. On one half of this AC signal voltage, the grid is made positive. On the other half cycle, the grid is made equally negative.

To examine in more detail what happens here, let us redraw the circuit. In this diagram, let us replace the antenna and tuning circuit with a simple alternating voltage generator.

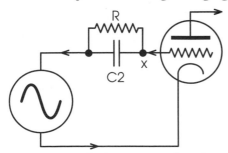

Figure 2.3 – Block Diagram of Grid Leak Detector Operation

In Figure 2.3, we are ignoring the plate circuitry for the present but will reconsider it later when we need it.

As is necessary, we will assume that the cathode of the tube is heated somehow, with a battery or otherwise, and is red hot. This red hot cathode is coated with a microscopic film of the chemical barium oxide which, when heated to red heat, boils off electrons as a hot tea kettle boils off steam.

When the grid of the tube is negative with respect to the cathode on the negative half cycle of the signal wave, the negative electrons streaming from the hot cathode are repelled by the negative grid. As granddad might say, you recall from science class that like charged objects hate each other's stink and thus repel each other.

On the other hand when the grid becomes positive the unlike charged electrons are attracted and rush over to the positive grid like flies toward spilled honey! This completes the electrical circuit between cathode and grid, and the electrons start flowing around the circuit as indicated by the arrows. As these electrons flow into the resistor, R, they make point x negative with respect the other end of the resistor and, as Ohm's law teaches us, develop a voltage drop across the resistor. Since capacitor C2 is connected directly across the resistor, it charges up and retains the voltage across it.

As time is passes, along comes another negative half cycle. No more electrons now flow from cathode to grid. The circuit is now open. Capacitor C2 cannot discharge through the tube but it does very slowly discharge through R which is of a high resistance value, usually several megohms. The capacitor maintains most of its charge and maintains a practically constant negative voltage on the grid as long as the AC signal voltage (represented by the generator in this diagram) does not change. This would be the case if the circuit were tuned to an AM broadcast station which for the moment was quiet.

Detection of AM Signals

When an announcer speaks, the circuitry in the broadcast transmitter causes the radiated wave to increase and decrease in magnitude in accordance with variations in the sound of the announcer's voice. Imagine that the generator in our model circuit no longer generates a steady signal. We can make it produce a signal which varies in amplitude like the sound of an announcer's voice. As the generator voltage varies, the charge in capacitor, C2, changes which in turn changes the voltage on the grid of the tube. If we were to replace the resistor, R, with a good pair of headphones, and if the station's signal is strong enough we may listen to the station's program just as if we were using a crystal set. In the place of the tube's grid and cathode, we could connect in a crystal detector fabricated from a chunk of galena and a cat whisker. Everything would work about the same because the grid-cathode circuit is acting as a rectifier just as the crystal detector does, only perhaps a bit more effectively. Both the crystal and the grid-cathode circuit of the tube will pass an electrical current through them in just one direction while blocking it in the other direction which is what a good rectifying detector is supposed to do.

Since the beginning of vacuum tube history, this circuit has been called a grid leak detector with resistor, R, being called the grid leak resistor.

Let's reassemble our detector circuit. We see in Figure 2.1 that the grid is located squarely between the cathode and the plate.

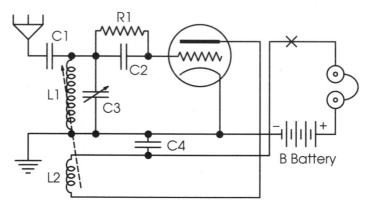

Figure 2.1 (repeated for reference) – Basic Regenerative Receiver

When we reconnect the battery and the phones, as in our original circuit, we see that the plate is now quite positively charged by the B battery. The positive plate attracts loose electrons from the hot cathode. A strong current now passes from the cathode to the plate, around through the phones and back to the battery.

Let's not forget the grid stands in the way of the electrons heading from cathode to plate. The grid acts like a traffic cop at the intersection of a busy road. Like the drivers on the road, the electrons must pay attention, as it were, to what the traffic cop grid dictates. With this in mind, let's see now how an AM voice signal and CW telegraph signals are reproduced in our headphones.

When a grid is only a little bit negative, the positive plate attracts the electrons much more strongly than an intensely negative grid repels them. So they easily dash through the spaces between the grid wires. When grid voltage goes negative, the grid repels the electrons more vigorously. The number of them that get through to the plate decreases. We see that by changes in the negative charge, the grid voltage has tight control upon the plate current which flows through the headphones.

When the grid voltage which is controlled by the charge on the grid capacitor, C2, is steady, a steady current flows through the phones.

When the announer speaks, the station's radiated signal changes accordingly. The charge upon capacitor, C2, and the voltage upon the grid change accordingly. As the grid voltage changes, the current flowing from cathode to plate of our tube changes. As this plate current changes so does the current through the phones. A changing current through the phones causes the diaphragms in them to vibrate and creating sound waves which closely resemble those of the announcer's voice. Thus, the program is recreated for us in the earphones.

In a practical vacuum tube circuit the battery current flowing in the plate circuit is many times, perhaps hundreds of times stronger than the rectified current produced by a weak radio signal in the grid circuit. This means that the current changes in the plate circuit will normally be much greater than the rectified current changes in the grid circuit. The tube thus amplifies the input signal, that is, makes it stronger. Indeed, a modern triode tube may amplify a signal by a factor of ten to a hundred times!

We have now discovered that, when connected by a grid leak detector, a single tube is actually a double purpose electronic tool. It is doing the two jobs. It is both detecting a signal and amplifying it at the same time. But it can do more.

Detection of CW Signals

We have just considered amplitude modulated voice signals. We must also consider CW radiotelegraph signals which are of importance to radio amateurs and others who are interested in the reception of very low powered signals at the greatest distances.

Unlike an amplitude modulated signal, a CW signal is a steady non-varying electromagnetic wave which, except for being broken up into dits and dahs by the transmitting operator's telegraph key, does not normally vary in intensity. When such a signal arrives at a simple non-regenerative grid leak detector, the detector will normally produce no response at all. Very strong signals might produce some thumps, hisses, or clicks, but little else. The constant amplitude of a continuous wave results in a constant charge being developed across the grid capacitor, resulting in a constant grid voltage. An unchanging grid voltage results in an invariant plate current. A constant current through a pair of headphones produces no sound.

To convert the dits and dahs into audible tones so they can be copied, we can make use of the process of "heterodyning." The result of heterodyning is an audio frequency signal called a "beat frequency" which can be amplified and fed to the headphones or loudspeaker. To create a beat frequency we will use a regenerative receiver that has been put into oscillation.

To hear these interesting signals with your regenerative detector, you must bring the tickler coil, L2, close to L1, the primary tuned coil, until the feedback is sufficient to put the circuit into oscillation. Doing so, reveals the third function of out little three-sided demon. We have already considered the first two of its signal reproducing functions, detection and audio amplification. Now we must speak of its duty as a heterodyne oscillator. To understand this function, let us use an acoustical analogy. Go to the piano and press down a key, say middle C at a frequency of 262 hertz. You will hear the note clearly. If you also step on the sustain pedal, the note will continue sounding. While middle C is sounding, strike the F key of 349, Hertz. As you listen to these two notes sounding together, the combination will sound different (if your piano is well tuned). With the sustain pedal pressed, forceably strike the same two keys, and listen carefully. If you have good ears and are observant, you should hear two additional tones, one being higher in pitch, at 611 Hertz. This is the sum of the original two frequencies, 262 plus 349. You may also hear yet another tone, at 87 Hertz, 349 minus 262. This may be more difficult to hear since your ears are not as sensitive at lower frequencies as they are at the higher ones. Whether or not you hear them, both of these two new tones are present. Musicians are well acquainted with this effect of mixing. The acoustic waves of the original two notes physically interfere with one another to produce the two new notes, or waves. These two new notes are called the beat frequency components.

Sum and Difference

An analogous phenomenon occurs in electrical systems. When two alternating current signals of different frequencies are combined in a nonlinear circuit, the output consists of the two original signals plus two new signals whose frequencies are equal to the sum and difference of the two original frequencies. The input circuit of a regenerative detector, being rectifying in nature, is definitely nonlinear. Beat frequency components are formed readily therein.

Suppose that the receiver is tuned to an incoming signal on say 10,000 kHz. If the regenerative detector circuit is oscillating and detuned just a bit, but not enough to lose the incoming signal, two new, beat frequency components will appear in the circuit. If our detector is oscillating at 10,000.5 kHz, one of the newly created signals will be at 20,000.5 kHz. Since it is almost twice the frequency of the original radio frequency signal, it will be greatly attenuated by the audio circuitry and, for all practical purposes, totally lost. The other new frequency, or beat component, will be at a frequency which is the difference of original frequencies, or 0.5 kHz (500 Hz). This is an audio frequency. It will be amplified by the audio circuitry, and will be heard in the headphones as a clear 500 Hz tone or whistle.

If you turn the tuning dial just a little until the detector is oscillating at 10,001 kHz, the two new frequencies will be 20,001 (the sum) and 1 kHz (the difference.) If the incoming signal is being keyed, that is broken in pieces of waves to form the dits and dahs of the morse code, you will hear in the phones short and long tones or whistles. A good radio operator can easily copy these tones. Through the years this process of beating an incoming signal against a signal generated locally by the detector's oscillation has come to be called heterodyning.

Heterodyning in Practice

We can say that the three functions which can be performed by a regenerative detector are detection, amplification and heterodyning, and it does all of them well. Suppose, with the detector oscillating you tune past an unmodulated carrier wave. You will first hear a very high pitched whistle as you approach the signal from one side. As the detector's oscillation frequency gets closer to the signal's frequency, the pitch of the whistle will drop. As you zero in on the exact frequency, the tone becomes lower and lower, in other words, the frequency difference between the two signals is becoming less and less.

When the detector's oscillating frequency becomes equal to that of the incoming signal, the whistle will completely disappear. As you continue to tune, you begin to move away from the signal. The difference between the two signals now begins to increase. Now the whistle will grow higher and higher in pitch until it becomes too high to be audible.

That point at which the whistle pitch reaches its lowest value and then disappears completely is called the zero beat point. We may represent this effect by a graph, as seen in Figure 2.5.

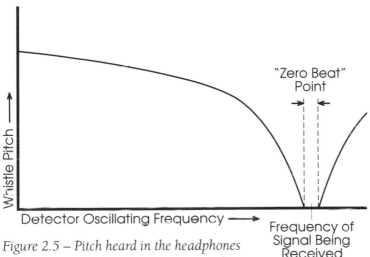

Figure 2.5 – Pitch heard in the headphones decreases as detector frequency comes closer to matching frequency of incoming signal.

If the dial of your receiver is accurately calibrated, you can determine the frequency of any incoming signal by tuning to the zero beat point, then reading its frequency from the frequency indicated on the dial. Or, if you know the frequency of an incoming signal, you can use it to check the calibration of your receiver's dial. It would be best to not to rely upon just one signal, but compare your dial readings with the known frequency of a number of signals, however.

Since what you hear in the earphones will be the dif-

45

ference between the frequencies of two radio frequencies, it should be apparent that a physically solid receiver capable of maintaining a stable frequency is highly desirable. If either the received CW signal is unstable, that is, changing in frequency slightly due to poor design of the transmitter, or your receiver is sloppily built and unstable, the resulting beat note will be rough, wobbly or both. Some homebuilt receivers do not perform well in this respect. You will want to build yours properly. Most amateur signals on today's high frequency bands are remarkably stable. So if many seem to wobble, drift in frequency, or chirp, it is probably your receiver's fault! When you design and build a regenerative receiver, plan to button things down tightly inside of it. A stable receiver is a joy to operate. An unstable one is a pain in the neck!

Part Three

Challenges of Regenerative Receiver Design

Electrical and Mechanical Stability Imperative

Along with solid physical construction, perhaps the most significant aspect of regenerative receiver construction is that of providing smooth, quiet and reliable control of the degree of regeneration. One may provide this either by controlling the amplification of the detector circuit or by increasing or decreasing the feedback ratio as defined earlier. It really makes little difference which type of regeneration control you choose so long as, first, it is stable and operates the way is should, and, second, does not significantly change the frequency of the regenerative detector's oscillation. It is almost impossible to change anything, including the degree of regeneration, without also changing the oscillation frequency. This is a fact of life that we must live with whether we like it or not. The object is, however, to minimize the interaction of the regeneration and tuning controls as much as possible.

Ways to Control Regeneration

There are at least a half dozen different ways of controlling regeneration, but a couple of them I would not recommend in practice. The rotatable tickler coil, or the plate vario-meter, was perhaps the first. But, in addition to being mechanically unwieldy, these usually viciously change the frequency to which the receiver is tuned. For these reasons let's not even consider these in our designs!

I also tend to be allergic to using a volume control potentiometer (pot) of the usual sort in any circuit carrying radio frequency signal currents. As their control shafts are rotated, pots frequency encounter noisy irregular spots in their resistive elements. They are not well suited for RF applications. So lets drop any scheme which requires RF in the pot itself.

There are at least three good methods, any of which, properly applied, will perform just fine. The choice becomes a matter of personal taste. I prefer the throttle capacitor method. Here, we connect a variable capacitor in se-ries with a tickler coil fixed in position on the coil form.

If you trace the path, in diagram of Figure 3.1, of the radio frequency feedback current from the tube's plate and through the tickler coil to the cathode, you will observe that the throttle capacitor is in series with it. As a rule, the greater the capacitance of a capacitor, the easier radio frequency current may pass

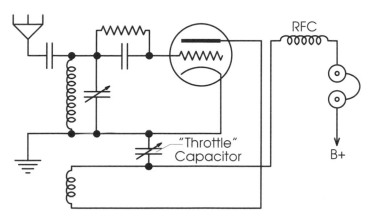

Figure 3.1 – My favorite way of controlling regeneration using a throttle capacitor

through it at any given frequency. By varying the capacitance, the opposition to the flow of the feedback signal through the throttle capacitor is changed, resulting in a change in the amount of feedback. The throttle capacitor gives us a neat, smooth way to control the amount of feedback signal reaching the tickler coil, and thus the regeneration. This method appeared in the "X-Circuit," designed by an engineer named Weagant shortly after the beginning of the twentieth century. I think that this was a great advance in regenerative radio design, and that Mr. Weagant's contribution should not be underestimated.

Quality Capacitors Needed

Most top quality variable capacitors manufactured for the radio market had quiet, smooth working bearings, which is an especially important requirement for a capacitor when used as a regeneration control. It must be possible to rotate the shaft of capacitor while generating negligible electrical noise. The control must smooth and quiet. Since 1975, the manufacture of quality variable capacitors has all but ceased. Often however, with a bit of scrounging, good ones, used of course, may often yet be found in old radio gear at radio swap meets, and the like.

A second advantage of this regeneration control method is that this regenerative circuit requires us to connect the rotary plates of the throttle capacitor firmly to circuit ground. Fortunately for us, the moving plates of variable capacitors are mechanically and electrically connected to the capacitor frame which is almost always mounted on a grounded bracket or panel.

Because of this, the rotation of a good capacitor's shaft is turned with neglibible electrical noise, and the control is smooth and quiet. A third advantage of this method is that a solidly grounded throttle capacitor reduces hand capacity – that annoying effect whereby the movements of one's body and hands affects the frequency to which the receiver is tuned. A small variable capacitor in the neighborhood of 100 picofarads maximum capacitance, usually suffices in the usual shortwave receiver.

Modifying AM Broadcast
Variable Capacitors

Although the precision midget variable capacitors so widely available years ago are now quite rare, we can use the variable capacitors common today. Unfortunately, most of these multiple plate variable capacitors have a capacitance range that is much too large for use in tuning shortwave receivers.

The tuning capacitor from a discarded AM broadcast receiver can be removed, modified to reduce its capacitance range, and successfully used in a receiver. Only those capacitors that use air as a dielectric can be modified. Those little, square capacitors with plastic dielectric universally used in transistor radios are all but useless for us.

A typical capacitor that is suitable for modification is shown in Figure 3.2. Our interest lies in the larger antenna section of plates.

First, remove the capacitor from the junk radio carefully in order to avoid bending any of the plates and thereby causing a short circuit within. Next, remove the mica insulated trimmers along the sides. We will have no use for these in our work. Note that electrical connection to the rotor plates is made through

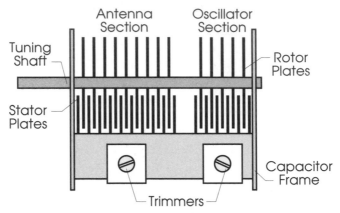

Figure 3.2 – Typical AM Broadcast Receiver Tuning Capacitor before modification

the capacitor frame. Electrical connection to either set of stator plates is made through respective soldering lugs located along the sides of the capacitor near the sites where the trimmers were once located.

In most cases the original maximum capacitance of the antenna section is usually about 365 picofarads which will tune the AM radio band from one end to the other. This value is far too large to use as a tuning capacitor in the short wave receivers we build. The exact capacitance value we need is not critical. Often one between 75 picofarads and 150 picofarads maximum will be most useful. This is roughly one third of the original capacitance.

To reduce the capacitance, leave the stator section strictly alone but carefully remove all but about one-third of the rotor plates. This can be done by grasping each plate to be removed firmly with a pair of long nosed pliers and by carefully pulling it straight out, much as a dentist extracts a tooth. Strive to damage the remaining plates as little as possible, of course.

When you have finished the extraction process, slowly rotate the remaining rotor plates into mesh with their matching stator plates while intently looking for plates that touch one another. If any touching does occur, carefully separate these plates with the small blade of a pocket knife. Scraping plates in a variable capacitor is a common bane of the receiver builder. You can avoid this irritating problem by first examining the plates by eye as they become meshed. Better yet run an electrical continuity check to be sure. Connect an ohmmeter between the capacitor frame and the stator plate soldering lug. Slowly rotate the tuning shaft from minimum (plates all the way out) to maximum capacitance (plates full meshed) and watch the ohmmeter. The meter needle should read its maximum, or open circuit, resistance value over the complete rotation range without even a flicker. If the meter needle does flicker, re-examine the plates again and make adjustments.

If you don't have an ohmmeter, connect a pair of magnetic headphones in series with a 1.5 volt flashlight battery and use this in its place. Put on the phones and rotate the capacitor shaft. Complete silence in the phones as you rotate the shaft through its range indicates a good capacitor ready for use.

A scraping capacitor is a common problem and one of the most throughly irritating. Prevent this unnecessary aggravation by carefully examining and testing your capacitor *before* installing it into your set.

Again, the unused plates in the stator section and oscillator section will not cause any problems. You can ignore them and use your modified tuning capacitor with confidence. Just be sure to connect the frame of the capacitor to the ground, B negative, tube cathode or FET source in the circuit to minimize troublesome hand capacity effects.

Choke Keeps RF Out of Audio Circuit

When this method of control is used, we must insert an additional inductor coil, a radio frequency choke (abbreviated RFC in the trade) between the regeneration throttle capacitor and the phones or audio amplifier in order to keep RF out of the audio section of the receiver. RFC's are still being sold, if you care to look for them or, you can make one. About two hundred turns of fine, insulated wire scramble wound around the body of a two watt carbon resistor (100 kilohms or greater in resistance) or a quarter inch wooden dowel rod, will do quite well. This is not in any way a critical item. But if you omit this choke coil, RF current may find its way to ground by some stray path and interfere with control of regeneration or cause trouble in other ways. Indeed, whatever type of regeneration control is used, the use of a choke coils is recommended. In passing, I feel that this throttle capacitor method of regeneration control is definitely the method, if other factors do not preclude its use.

Potentiometer Control of Regeneration

There are receiver designs, however, in which the use of some kind of potentiometer regeneration control works well. When this method is used, it is most advantageous to use the pot, often just a garden variety volume control, to vary the DC plate voltage applied to the tube, as illustrated in Figure 3.3.

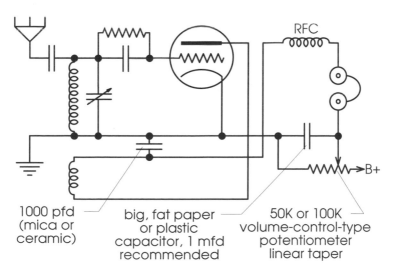

| 1000 pfd (mica or ceramic) | big, fat paper or plastic capacitor, 1 mfd recommended | 50K or 100K volume-control-type potentiometer linear taper |

Figure 3.3 – Controlling Regeneration by Changing Plate Voltage with a Potentiometer

It has been found that when a "modern" triode tube, one made since 1920 let's say, is chosen, its operating characteristics when used as an audio amplifier change very little when the DC plate voltage is changed, particularly within the ten to fifty volt range, a range most suitable for regenerative detector use. But a triode's ability to oscillate at radio frequencies *does* vary with the applied voltage. Therefore, we can keep the feedback coupling between tickler and tuned coil physically constant and precisely control the degree of regeneration by controlling the DC plate voltage.

Since the control potentiometer is located in the DC circuitry, its ability to make unpleasant scraping and scratching noises as the shaft is turned is greatly reduced. All potentiometers we are likely to use are somewhat noisy and become more so with use. To eliminate this problem we can install a bypass capacitor where shown in the schematic diagram. Since its purpose is to shunt audio noise to ground, a suitable value would be in the neighborhood of one microfarad. A smaller value may not eliminate the noise. A much larger value may make the regeneration control "mushy", or create a kind of backlash effect.

I have had very good luck with this particular system of control; make no mistake about it. And while I have no first hand experience, I understand that this method of control also works well in junction FET transistor circuits. So, try it for yourself and see.

Control of Screen Voltages

The third method of regeneration control that I can confidently recommend performs beautifully, but requires the use of a screen-grid or a pentode tube. In application, it is quite similar to the method just described, Here, however, it is the screen grid voltage (grid no. 2) that is controlled by the potentiometer. The plate voltage remains fixed. The plate current in multi-grid tubes is relatively unaffected by changes in the DC plate voltage. Changes in the screen-grid voltage, however, have a very great effect on the plate current.

See the "Pentode-Triode" Receiver described on page 102 as an example of screen grid voltage control.

In other words, the screen-grid voltage has almost complete control over the DC plate current. Since it is the plate current that is directly related to the regeneration, we see that controlling the screen DC voltage precisely controls the circuit's regeneration.

Two Bypass Capacitors Recommended

It is a good idea to connect two different by pass capacitors from the screen grid terminal to ground. The first of these should be a radio frequency bypass, a mica or ceramic capacitor of about 5000 picofarads and physically located as close to the screen grid connection as possible. The second capacitor, a bypass of one microfarad, paper or plastic, may be physically located anywhere convenient in the parts layout in order to eliminate potentiometer noise. Also, particularly where a higher voltage power supply is being used, say 150 to 400 volt, it becomes necessary to insert an additional fixed resistor between the "hot side" of the regeneration control potentiometer and the power supply's high voltage B+ point. In most cases a two watt, 47 kilohm resistor will serve here very well.

Lower Frequencies
Recommended for Beginners

Of all the vexations which seem to arise within homebuilt regenerative receivers, those associated with the coils seem to be the most puzzling and troublesome. In this discussion, we talk about problems with coils wound for a short wave regenerative receiver designed to be used between the approximately three and fifteen MHz. While experienced builders may have success with regenerative receivers at higher frequencies, the usual coil problems which arise become much more difficult beyond 15 MHz. As a result I do recommend that you stick with the lower frequencies until you have acquired some experience. Likewise, to push the lower frequency limit down into the AM broadcast band, 540 to 1620 kHz, will no doubt get you music and talk radio, but a regenerative receiver won't deliver top rate audio quality. Regeneratives "strut their stuff" in the three to fifteen MHz bands. There are plenty of signals in this range to keep you busy.

Coil Problems

Coil problems may be classified broadly as either conceptual or mechanical. Conceptual design problems arise either because the builder does not understand the principles of feedback and how to use it, or he does not properly understand the nature of electrical resonance and its relationship to inductance and capacitance.

Let us examine feedback first. In order for a regenerative receiver to work at all, its regeneration control must be able to bring the degree of feedback smoothly to the point of oscillation and a bit more. In terms of coil winding, this generally means that the turns ratio between the tickler and tuned coil (often called the secondary coil) must be correct. Secondly, there must be a reasonable amount of physical separation between these two coils as they exist on the coil form. Finally, the connections to the coils must be poled correctly, as old timers used to say. In other words the magnetic polarity must be correct.

As discussed earlier, we must be able to bring the degree of regeneration smoothly up to, and a bit past, the point of circuit oscillation with precise control. Not only must we provide a strong enough feedback signal, but also the polarity of the feedback of the signal induced in the secondary coil by the tickler must be such that voltages add up rather than subtract. We can insure this magnetic polarity in typical solenoid coils by making the connections as shown in Figure 3.4.

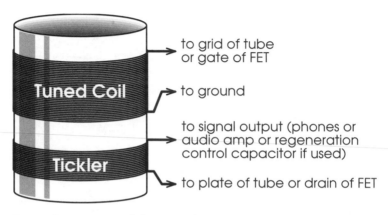

Figure 3.4 – *Heart of the Typical Regenerative Receiver: The Tuning Coil and its Tickler*

It makes "a whale of a difference" how these coils are connected. If you reverse the connections on one of the coils, all the king's horses and all the queen's men will not be able to make the circuit oscillate! In fact, should you make this reversal, not only will the circuit not oscillate, increasing the amount of feedback will decrease the probability of it oscillating! Positive feedback is absolutely required here. These polarity requirements will remain the same for any cylindrical coil pair, regardless of their size.

This was a matter of profound confusion during my youth because when winding a coil without really understanding the principles, you have a 50-50 chance of getting things wrong. I usually did. My friends couldn't help me either. Feedback theory was not included in the physics course at the high school we attended.

Rules for Numbers of Turns

The number of turns needed for the tuned, or secondary, coil depends on the size of the tuning capacitor in the circuit and the frequency you wish to cover. So how do you estimate the number of turns needed for the tickler? Once upon a time, a common rule of thumb seemed to be:

- for coils of ten turns or more, put one third as many turns upon the tickler as appear upon the tuned winding
- for nine to five turns on the tuned winding put one half as many upon the tickler
- for less than five turns, make the tuned coil and tickler the same

That was probably satisfactory for the older tubes which were not as hot performers as newer ones are. It also compensated for many of faults that we duffers of the time unknowingly made while building our sets.

For tubes marketed after about 1940, the tickler sizes recommended are usually too large resulting in the regeneration control becoming critical. And if it is turned up too far, "grid blocking" occurs, and the most horrific howling and squealing occurs, called "squegging" in more refined circles! For instance, in the extremely useful Lindsay Publications reprint, *The 1934 Official Short Wave Radio Manual,* many of the coil specifications therein call for a tickler coil with twice as many turns as are needed today. But back in 1934, the year I received my first FCC Amateur Radio License, we kids seemed to have a hard time making our detectors oscillate at all. Maybe the authors had us in mind.

As for the coil separation, we can draw on another rule-of-thumb. Experience indicates that a tickler coil of fewer turns positioned closer to the tuned coil provides better control than a tickler of more turns positioned away. In my opinion, these coils need never be separated by more than 3/8 inch at the most, and should actually be closer together. Coils, if too close, can link not only magnetically, but capacitively as well. In the last coil winding illustration, the points of low RF potential on each coil are adjacent reducing the problem of excess capacitive coupling.

Many radio publications, particularly older ones, show tuned coils for the higher frequency bands as having their turns separated by greater than the wire diameter. They called this spaced winding. It became a sort of "Holy Dogma" at that time and was widely used.

Since then, except for the most critical situations, this has now been largely discredited. I find the simpler, closely spaced turns as effective and much easier to wind neatly.

"XP-53" COIL FORMS AND KITS

Outstanding forms using new low loss insulation material—XP-53. Natural coloring eliminating losses. Groove-ribbed for air spaced windings. Flange grips, meter indexes. Moulded threaded shelf in form. 1½" diameter and 2⅞" long exclusive of prongs. Kits with wound coils for MC-140-M condenser also available.

CODE	LIST
SWF-4 (four prongs, coil form only)..........$ .35
SWF-5 (five prongs, coil form only).......... .35
SWF-6 (six prongs, coil form only)..................... .40
No. 40 coil (wound coil, 4 prongs, 10-20 meters)........ 1.00
No. 41 coil (wound coil, 4 prongs, 17-41 meters) 1.00
No. 42 coil (wound coil, 4 prongs, 33-75 meters) 1.00
No. 43 coil (wound coil, 4 prongs, 66-150 meters)........ .75
No. 44 coil (wound coil, 4 prongs, 135-270 meters)........ .75
BCC-4 (wound coil, 4 prongs, 250-560 meters)............ 1.25
No. 60 coil (wound coil, 6 prongs, 10-20 meters).......... 1.25
No. 61 coil (wound coil, 6 prongs, 17-41 meters)......... 1.25
No. 62 coil (wound coil, 6 prongs, 33-75 meters)......... 1.25
No. 63 coil (wound coil, 6 prongs, 66-150 meter) 1.00
No. 64 coil (wound coil, 6 prongs, 135-270 meters)........ 1.00
BCC-6 (wound coil, 6 prongs, 250-560 meters)............ 1.50
SWK-4 (kit—4, four-prong coils, 17-270 meters)............ 3.00
SWK-6 (kit—4, six-prong coils, 17-270 meters)............ 3.75

Figure 3.5 – Hammarlund Plug-In Coil Forms as advertised in the 1939 Radio Amateur's Handbook

Part Four

Building a Practical Regenerative Receiver

Wire Size for Coils

As for the size of wire to be used, for receiver use, I see no need for wire larger than No. 26, B&S gauge. When more turns are needed, smaller wire, no.'s 24 or 26 gauge may work better, and be satisfactorily used. Use cotton or silk-covered wire, if you can get it, but this is hard to find today. An excellent source of coil wire, and even antenna wire, is your friendly local electric motor repair shop which usually stocks magnet wire of good quality in many different sizes. Often, if you are polite to the gentlemen there, they may sell you what you need for much less than charged for at radio parts store.

Determining the number of turns of wire required upon a coil form of a given size such that it will tune to a given frequency with a given capacitance is far more difficult problem than most people think. Just use the inductance formula you find in one of the radio handbooks or in the appendix of this book, punch in the data into your pocket calculator and read out the number of turns you need! Those who tend to worship mathematics but who do not understand it very well often use formulas like this and are usually disappointed. The trouble is that in order for the formulas to give you an accurate answers, you must be sure that your coil meets all the prerequisite conditions upon which the formula is based. Secondly, the data must be correct, and this is often hard to be sure of, particularly with a small coil. Finally, almost all of the common inductance formulas available to us, that is not the complex formulas you might find in the Bureau of Standards Bulletins, fail miserably for coils shorter than their diameter, as most of the coils we wind are. I once did some fooling around, sometimes called informal research on this topic, so I can speak from experience. The best advice I can give here would be to examine several samples of published coil data which at least approximately resemble what you have in mind. Use your common sense. Then cut and try until things tune as you wish them to do.

Plug-In Coil Forms

It is generally agreed that, for the home builder, plug-in coils, one for each high frequency band of interest, are the way to go. Fancy coil switching setups are all right for experienced engineers with extensive shop facilities but are usually beyond our reach and are probably not worth the trouble anyway. What can we use for coil forms? During my youth, beautifully colored, fluted plastic coil forms were universally available for a reasonable price! But where are these today? They have "gone with the snows of yesteryear." One long shot is the junk box of an old time radio amateur. These sometimes turn up at radio flea markets, that is, hamfests, but you can't count on this. Sockets in which to plug the coils can be hard to find. Even tubes are become more difficult to find, although many types are still being manufactured in foreign countries.

Look around in junk shops, thrift shops, the back rooms of older radio TV repair shops, and the junk boxes of older amateurs. See if you can get your hands upon some of those old glass tubes which have four prongs protruding from their bases. Common types were type 45, type 80, type 2A3, type 5Z3, type 01A, type 71A, type 12A, type 10, type 50, type 26, and type 83 or 83V. Some of these are quite rare since they are "collectibles" and thus sought after by antique radio collectors who often pay exorbitant prices for them.

Figure 4.1 – Old Tube Bases Used as Plug-In Coil Forms

All you will need are three tubes. It makes no difference if they are burned out or even broken. All we need are their bases (Fig. 4.1). Once you have three of them, put them into a saucepan, cover with water, put them on the kitchen stove and (with mama's permission) boil them for an hour or so. Then fish them out of the water. Take the base in one hand, and the bulb in the other and twist. The base should loosen easily and come clear of the bulb. Finally, take your soldering iron in hand and unsolder the end of each pin upon the base of each tube. When the solder is molten, give the base a sharp flip and all of the solder should fly out. Be careful! Hot solder, even a drop or so, can give someone standing nearby a nasty burn! You have three nice forms, for three plug in coils, that would make any good radio amateur of the late 1920's or early 1930's jump with joy! They should make you happy too.

[Think twice before you cannabalize older vacuum tubes. Many are becoming quite scarce since they are no longer manufactured and because interest in oldtime radio has dramatically increased in recent years among collectors. When Rock was writing magazine articles in the 1950's, four prong tubes were very common, and transistors were extremely scarce. Times have changed.
An excellent source of coil forms and tubes for me has been hamfests, and obsolete telephone radio equipment in local scrap yards. You may be able to get by with octal tube bases which were common into the 50's and 60's although "Rock" considers their smaller diameter not as desireable. These tubes are still quite easy to find. –editor]

Having your coil forms, now what do you do with them? If you have heated the end of each prong and have carefully flipped all of the solder out of each of them, you should be able to look down into each form and clearly see light through every cylindrical prong. They should all be clear of solder. Then clamp each make-shift coil form carefully (care is a watch-word in good radio construction) in your vise, and using a hacksaw with a fine toothed blade, saw a slit down the side of each form. Do not cut into the disk at the bottom of the form which supports the pins! You can cut the slit at any point in relation to the prongs, but in the interests of uniformity, slit each form in the same way.

Designing the Coils

You are now ready to wind your three coils that together will cover the 15 to 100 meter portion of the radio frequency spectrum. How many turns upon each coil? As we have implied, if you insist on great precision here, you will be disappointed. First, there are too many indeterminate factors involved. The exact capacitance range of the tuning capacitor you plan to use in your receiver is an unknown variable. Even more poorly known are stray circuit capacitances and wiring inductances, the grid to cathode capacitance of the tube, the effects of the interaction with the tickler coil, and others. And that doesn't mention the inaccuracies of most inductance formulas.

What about the frequency or tuning range

which we might expect to cover with each coil? Referring to that good old resonance formula with which our science teacher so vexed us,

$$f = \frac{1}{2\pi\sqrt{LC}}$$

we observe that the tuning range will be a function of the square root of the capacitance range. In other words, if we were to increase the value of the capacitance (or inductance) by a factor of four, the resonant frequency would by cut by a factor of the square root of four, or a factor of two. If we plan upon using the typical short wave tuning capacitor of 100 picofarads maximum and estimate the minimum capacitance of the circuit to be about 20 picofarads, the theoretical tuning span will be about two to one.

In practice however, we do not use the entire range of a variable capacitor because the two ends of its capacitance range are non linear. In other words rotating the shaft of the capacitor near the ends of its range, does not produce completely predictable changes in capacitance. In practice, the real tuning range is closer to 1.7 to one. Thus, we might expect the coverage of each coil to be approximately 15 to 9 MHz, 9 to 5 MHz, and 5 to 3 MHz. If we calculate the inductance of each coil using the low frequency of each coil with 100 pfd of capacitance, we arrive at values of about 3 microhenrys, 10 microhenrys and 28 microhenrys, respectively. Then, using one of the many inductance formulas available, we can calculate the number of turns needed for each: 5 turns, 15 turns and 35 turns. Interestingly enough, these numbers come quite close to the average number of turns on 1 1/4 inch form described in the popular literature on similar projects. Assuming that we'll be using a modern triode or junction FET, we can choose the number of turns for the tickler coil in each case and arrive at the coil table 4.2.

Nominal Wave Length	No. Turns Tuned Coil	No. Turns Tickler Coil
20-34 Meters	5	2
40-60 Meters	15	3
80-100 Meters	35	6

Figure 4.2 – Typical Coil Parameters

Again, these turn values assume the use of a 100 picofarad maximum capacitance. And this is a capacitor very often used in short-wave receiver construction. If a 140 picofarad capacitor is used, these will remain useable but the tuning range covered by each will be a bit different. Remember that to get top performance, each coil may have to be individually "tweaked." This is especially necessary for the tickler coils. The estimate values will serve as a starting point in our process of cut-and-try design.

If enamel insulated magnet wire is used to wind the coils, be sure to sand off the enamel where the wire is to be soldered or connected to in any way. This detail is not always obvious. I knew a number of young people who desperately tried to solder right over the enamel. Use hard-to-find silk or cotton covered wire, if you can get it.

Wire as slender as No. 26 B&S gauge can be used where many turns are needed. When plenty of winding space is available upon each form, you might find a larger gauge wire easier to work with, possibly No. 22 gauge. Considering the range of wire sizes and our level of imprecision, the wire size makes little difference in frequency or performance.

Wind the Coils

Start with the tuned coil. Pass the cleaned end of the wire through the slot and through one of the form's prongs and out the end. Bend it over to hold it in place. Clamp the wire spool in a vise. Run off four or five feet of wire, and pull it taut. Then closely wind the specified number of turns. There should be no space between adjacent turns. We call this a "close wound coil." Hold the windings on the form tightly with your finger, and snip the wire. Sand enamel off the end, and pass this through another prong and out the end. Using rosin-core solder, fill each pin with hot solder, and allow each to cool. Snip off any excess wire protruding from each prong. This should complete the tuned coil.

Next, repeat this general winding procedure to create the tickler coil. Be sure to wind both coils in the same direction. *This is vital!* Position the bottom turn of the tickler about 1/8 inch away from the edge of the tuned winding. You may choose the pin connection scheme you prefer but the I suggest the arrangement shown in Figure 4.3. This has been my way of winding and connecting coils for many, many years.

Wind and connect all coils the in the same way, otherwise you may become very confused later! You will plug the completed coil into a standard tube socket. If you wire the socket as follows, you should never have a problem making the circuit regenerate and oscillate, assuming, of course, that the rest of the circuit is correctly built:

Pin 1 – Grid (or gate of FET).
Pin 2 – Cathode (or source of FET).
Pin 3 – audio output (or regeneration control capacitor if variable).
Pin 4 – Plate (or drain of FET)

How I wish someone would have given me a diagram like this during my callow youth! How many tears and curses could have been avoided!

Most authors, when describing how tube base coils are constructed, prefer to drill individual holes in the form for each wire to pass through. But I came upon the slot technique

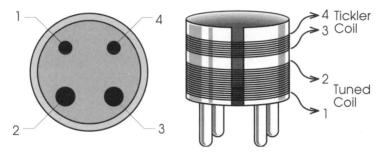

Figure 4.3 – Winding the Coils on a Tube Socket Base.

I'm recommending 62 years ago, and I have used it ever since. But use your own judgement here. Perhaps you can devise a better way to wind coils.

When you have wound and tested the coils, give each of them a light coat of clear lacquer. If you handle them carefully you will find that they will serve you in other regenerative receivers as well for years to come.

Antenna May Cause Dead Spots

Another important topic, directly related to coil winding, is the coupling of the antenna to the receiver. Many, possibly even most, simple regenerative receivers described in radio literature, couple the antenna through a very small capacitor of 10 pfd or less directly to the grid end of the tuned coil. Although this often does work well, there are problems which can arise.

First, there may be "dead spots." These are unique resonant frequencies at which the antenna sucks out so much energy from the tuned circuit that the detector will not oscillate well, if at all. When the coupling capacitance IS reduced to make the detector oscillate at these resonant frequencies, the capacitance is often too small to offer enough coupling on all the other trouble-free frequencies. Changing the length of the antenna and thereby changing its natural resonant frequency often helps. This may be physically inconvenient or impossible if the antenna is a dipole. It can be difficult even if you use a fairly long single wire.

One excellent solution to the problem that I have found is the use of loose magnetic coupling. This can be achieved by winding another coil about twice the diameter of the plug-in coils consisting of a few turns of hook up

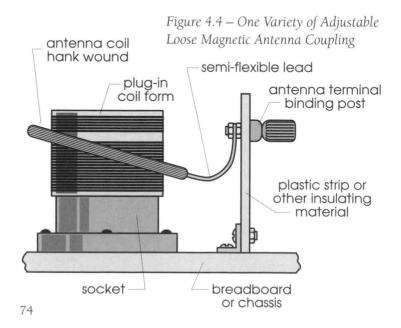

Figure 4.4 – One Variety of Adjustable Loose Magnetic Antenna Coupling

antenna coil hank wound

semi-flexible lead

plug-in coil form

antenna terminal binding post

plastic strip or other insulating material

socket

breadboard or chassis

or bell wire in "hank form", that is, with turns bunched and tied or cemented together with household glue. Often times, a single turn of heavy wire will give ample coupling. This coupling coil can be mounted on a separate support so as to be concentric with the regular receiver plug-in coil, in other words, a coil within a coil. Or the coupling coil can be supported by its connections. It may be designed in some way so that the coupling between it and the receiver coil may be adjusted.

When this new coil is adjusted and connected to your dipole or long wire, the coupling will be "tight" enough for all frequencies to allow good signal transfer, but will be "loose" enough at troublesome resonant frequencies to minimize the dead spots and even possibly eliminate them.

Capacitive coupling of the antenna to the detector often creates another problem. It is possible to get electromagnetic coupling between the antenna and the operator's body by way of the headphone cord which then feeds the signal back into the set. (All *good* radio men use head phones for serious listening. Loud speakers are for casual listening or mere entertainment only.)

Hand Capacity Causes Instability

The hand capacity is a most disturbing effect. Because of electrostatic coupling between the operator's body and hands and coil-capacitor tuning circuit, the frequency to which the receiver is tuned can be changed by changing the position of the operator's body and hands!

Other kinds of instability may sometimes occur. Magnetic antenna coupling used with a good ground connected to the set chassis usually eliminates this problem also.

A solidly grounded metallic front panel will act as a very effective shield in reducing hand capacity effects. But a solid ground is very important. If the ground lead from the set to a water pipe or grounding rod is very long, it may not provide adequate grounding. Small diameter wires have small but measurable inductance. Flat ribbons or surfaces such as the shielding braid of coaxial cable have far less inductance, and are superior when used in grounding regenerative receivers. The difference is grounding ability between a simple wire and a ribbon can be quite noticeable.

Phones or Speaker?

Is an audio amplifier following the regenerative detector really needed? This is often a personal decision. An amplifier is imperative if a loud speaker is to be used. In my opinion, an amplifier is an unnecessary luxury for a simple receiver but not out of the question. Some of us can find real enjoyment in the intelligent use of a good one tube set. I recall a particular one-tuber which used a single type '30 tube and which sat beside my bed during my youth. Many were the distant amateur stations I copied while lying, phones on head, there in the dark of a cold winter's night! But! For a one-tuber to perform well, you must have an excellent pair of old style magnetic high-impedance headphones, and these are difficult to find these days. New stereo headphones are of no use for us. Their electrical impedance is much too low. True, a special matching transformer can be used that offers high impedance to the detector and low impedance to the 'phones, but these transformers are also often hard to get. Also, modern earphones are designed with a broad frequency response for high quality music reproduction, *not* high signal sensivity. Good high-impedance radio 'phones are best when they have a response of 300-3000 Hz.

Even if you add a simple stage of audio amplification to your set, a sensitive pair of headphones is a distinct advantage and are actually a valuable part of your receiver. Look around in well stocked antique or thrift stores and in your grandmother's or old Uncle Ben's attic. Maybe you'll find an old pair. These are often very good.

Never buy a second-hand pair without first testing them – "caveat emptor", remember? How does one properly test a pair of phones for serious use? An ohm meter may say they are good, but this means little. Many years ago Hugo Gernsback recommended the following helpful test: In a quiet room, put the phones over your ears. Next, wet the metal tips at the ends of the phone cord and scratch them together. An easily heard click, or series of clicks usually indicates a reasonably sensitive pair. I've wondered if the 'phones huckstered by Mr. Gernsback's radio parts company, The Electro Importing Company, would pass this test? I assume that they would have. And, when you finally do get a good pair of headphones, baby them! They are a sensitive, precision instrument.

Field Effect Transistors
in Place of Vacuum Tubes

Although a junction FET makes a remarkably good regenerative detector and is a pleasure to work with, it usually will not without additional amplification develop a strong enough signal in most phones. Adding another junction FET as an audio amplifier will solve this problem most adequately.

For both vacuum tube triode or a JFET circuits, an interstage audio transformer is needed to couple the detector to the amplifier. An old, *old* transformer, salvaged from Aunt Minnie's discarded neutrodyne will do very well. *[I think this is another case of where you need to think twice before cannabalizing - editor]* If you find one, test both primary and secondary windings with an ohmmeter to make sure that they have not opened up before you install the transformer in your set.

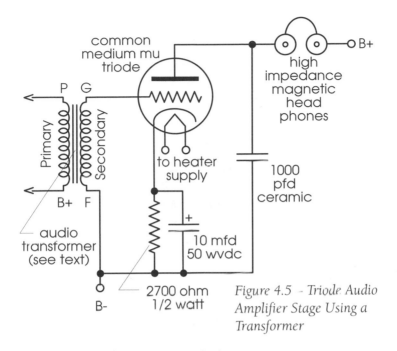

Figure 4.5 - Triode Audio Amplifier Stage Using a Transformer

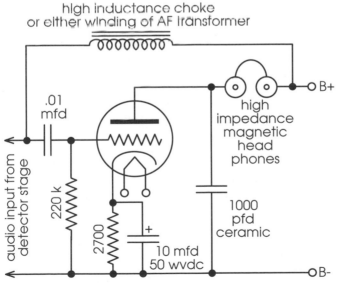

Figure 4.6 – Audio Amplifier Stage coupled through an audio frequency choke to the detector.

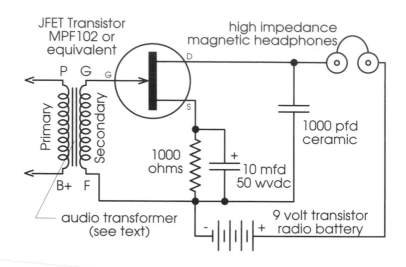

Figure 4.7 – Field Effect Transistor Amplifier Stage

You need, in either case, a tube type interstage transformer. Transistor types are utterly useless here! A diagram for a simple single stage audio amplifier suitable for use with a regenerative detector is shown in Figures 4.5 and 4.6.

A simple amplifier stage suitable for use with a JFETcircuit is shown in Figure 4.7. This amplifier stage is particularly helpful when it follows a regenerative detector using a JFET transistor.

Diagrams for other types of audio amplifiers are easily found in old radio literature. The Lindsay reprint, *SW Radio Quiz-Book and Kinks,* is replete with them, and other pertinent information also. Either a two-tube or two junction-FET regenerative receiver will "fill a pair of good phones with signals" when used with a good antenna. But if you really need loud signals, a more complex and expensive amplifier is needed. But this is beyond the scope of our discussion.

The physical details of the receiver we have been discussing are a matter of personal taste. You may demand the height of sophistication and swank. But I'm a simple soul and demand nothing of that nature.

Build the Receiver Like a Battleship

One design rule is imperative. No matter how you build your regenerative receiver, it must be rock solid – as solid as a battleship! The performance of so many commercial and homebuilt regenerative receivers has been utterly undermined by their flimsy construction. As we have said, any mechanical or electrical change that even slightly affects the circuitry will shift the frequency to which it is tuned. There is no way around this problem. This is just the nature of the Beast! I have seen, perhaps maybe even once built, such sets that were so mechanically deficient that a visitor walking across the room would de-tune the receiver by his mere presence. Such a thing is avoidable and, therefore, inexcusable! Now this does not mean that a fancy, expensive metal cabinet is a necessity, by no means. Unless you live in an exceptionally electrically noisy neighborhood, "tight shielding" promoted by some experts, that is, a receiver completely enclosed in a metal cabinet, is not needed. The only shielding that should be used is the metallic front panel. And I don't endorse attempts at miniaturization. I think it's unnecessary and just more glitz!

Years ago we all built receivers upon a 3/4 inch thick wooden board with a batten at each end to prevent warping and with a galvanized iron or aluminum front panel cut for us at the local tin-smith's shop. If you give the board a coat of walnut varnish stain and the panel a coat of spray lacquer, it does not look at all bad. It may be a bit "old fashioned" but who are we trying to fool? Only those experimenters wrapped up in the state of the art to the degree that everything must bear the cyberspace touch might be offended. But then, these experimenters don't build regenerative receivers.

Slow-Motion Vernier Dial Drive Essential

One thing that a top quality regenerative receiver absolutely requires is a quality slow motion dial drive. You must be able to open and close the plates of the tuning capacitor very precisely using one of these speed-reduction dials. Without a vernier dial, the tuning is so rapid, you could scarcely hope to tune in all of those weak, far away foreign signals that a good receiver is capable of bringing in. Once upon a time these dials were common, but, like so many items that we have mentioned

Figure 4.8 – National Radio Products advertised these dials in the 1939 Radio Amateur's Handbook.

1a – 1 5/8" "HRO" dial
1b – 3 1/2" "O" dial
2 – Precision Dials, Type N, have engine divided scales and verniers of solid German Silver. The Verniers are flush, eliminating errors from parallax.
3 – The four-inch Type N dial employs a smooth and powerful planetary mechanism with a 5 to 1 ratio. No. 2, 3, 4 or 5 scale.
4 – The original "Velvet Vernier" Dial, Type A, is still an unchallenged favorite for general purpose use. It is exceptionally smooth and entirely free from backlash. The mechanism is contained within the bakelite knob and shell. Ratio 5 to 1. No. 2, 4 or 5 scale in 4" diameter. No. 2 scale in 3 3/8" diameter.
5 – The BM Dial (Fig. 5) is a smaller version of the Type B Dial for use where space is limited. It is similar to the Type B Dial in appearance and mechanism, but does not have the variable-ratio device. No. 1 or 5 scales.
6 – "Velvet Vernier" Dial, Type B (Fig 6) provides a compact variable ratio drive that is smooth and trouble free. The mechanism is inclosed in a black bakelite case, the dial being read through a window. No. 1 or 5 scales.

which are important to us traditional radio builders, these are growing scarce. The Japanese make some neat, planetary drive dials which were, until recently, available at radio jobbers. But these cost an arm and a leg! I prefer the older, slow-motion dials which I have found are still available at some private, small parts dealers at a more reasonable price. When these old dials are cleaned up with a bit of lacquer thinner, they can shine like new.

However, you decide to build your set, remember to fasten everything down tightly so that nothing can move and certainly not break loose. In the electronics classes I once taught I used to require that my student's projects pass what we called the "****ivity Test." What you do is take out the tubes and drop the device on the floor from a three foot height. If nothing breaks loose and if the receiver still works properly when the tubes are replaced, the receiver really has "****ivity." Your receiver should have "****ivity" also.

We have mentioned regenerative receivers built with transistors, especially junction FET transistors. Rarely will you seen any radio construction articles that use modern devices like FET's to build very early radio circuits like regeneratives. Most the circuits you find describe superheterodynes and transceivers for more advanced radio amateurs. But I can fix this problem.

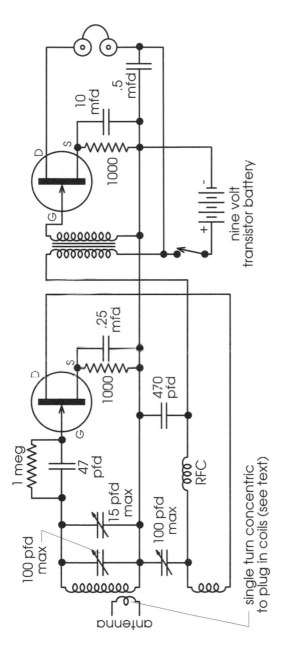

Figure 4.9 – Solid State Equivalent of Classic
"Doerle" Regenerative Receiver From the 1930's

Solid State Doerle Receiver

Shown in Figure 4.9 is a schematic diagram for a two JFET transistor receiver which I recently built. I call it the solid state Doerle, after a very famous two-tube receiver from the 1930's, of great popularity which was described in *Short Wave Craft* magazine during my youth. This space-age solid-state version performs about as well as the original, two-tube Doerle receiver did, I think.

A brief description of this receiver might be in order. It was built upon a 5 inch by 9 1/4 inch by 3/4 inch stained pine board with a 3/4 inch by 5 inch batten under each end (Fig. 4.10). A galvanized iron panel, 6 inches by 9 inches, sprayed with brown lacquer was used as a front panel. Had it been available, an aluminum panel might have done well here also. The audio frequency transformer was an ancient Thordarson with a 3 to 1 step up ratio. Who knows how old it might be! It was "liberated" from some discarded broadcast receiver. On the front panel is an old Pilot slow-motion vernier dial drive mounted in the center connected to the 15 pfd variable capacitor being used as a bandspread capacitor. On the left side is a knob controlling the 100 pfd regeneration control capacitor while another knob on the right side operates the bandset capacitor.

To use the set, the bandset capacitor is set to the edge of the desired amateur band, in

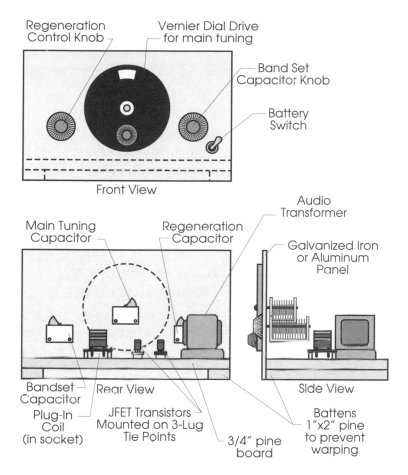

Figure 4.10 – *Two JFET Regenerative Receiver*

effect, quickly and approximately tuning the receiver to the desired frequency range. Once set, the 15 pfd bandspread capacitor and vernier dial drive make very small variations in the frequency. The stations are spread out across the dial, making it far easier to zero in on a particular signal. Again, the bandset capacitor is very coarse tuning with the bandspread capacitor being used for final fine tuning. This was a very common technique used in receivers designed for use by radio amateurs.I highly recommend it.

The headphones and antenna were connected to the set with Fahnstock clips screwed to the board. Remember Fahnstock clips? If not, examine an old radio parts catalog or radio construction articles. They were "essential" components in the old days. Believe it or not, I still have a few around. I love 'em.

The power switch was mounted on the lower right hand corner of the front panel. Three plug-in coils for the 20, 40 and 80 meter amateur bands were wound using the techniques we have already covered. The two JFET transistors were purchased from Radio Shack. Very common MPF102 JFETS may be substituted if desired. The transistors were soldered to three-lug terminal strips screwed to the board.

I was pleased with the performance of this receiver which, I think, closely approached the performance of a traditional two-tube receiver. This seems to demonstrate that, is so desired, JFET transistors may be effectively substituted for tubes. As a bonus transistors require no expensive power supply. An inexpensive, nine volt transistor battery is all that is necessary. I sent this receiver to a young friend of mine who is studying for his amateur radio license examination. He is using it to practice copying morse code found on the amateur bands.

"Rock's Own Blooper"

Not having actually built a regenerative receiver for some time now, I felt as though I should. So I did.

My "blooper" is built into a cast aluminum chassis which once contained a crazy gadget called a Workrite Multi-Unit many, many years ago. This is thus a true "Scotsman's Delight" since it cost me virtually nothing but my time, some solder and some bell wire.

The circuit and its various component values are about what I recommend in my mini-sized Magnum Opus. Anything different follows because I didn't have the specified value on hand but used what I did have instead within reasonable and proper limits. This just goes to show how non-critical a blooper can be!

How does the little set work? Well, I believe that I can hear just about anything that anyone can with any kind of receiver. This includes zillions of ham CW signals from all over creation.

The first "Blooper"

Build yourself an inexpensive little blooper, hook it onto a short, piece of wire. Then... Wow! The tooting and whistling of myriads of amateurs, the roar of ship and shore stations and the boom of broadcasters from all over our planet will pour into your phones! What an adventure! And it needn't cost you an arm and a leg, either.

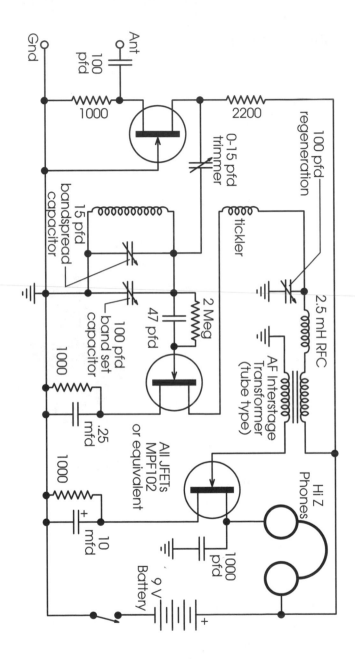

Figure 4.11 – "Rocks's Own Blooper", an inexpensive field-effect transistor receiver

Yesterday afternoon, from about 5:15 to 5:45, CDST on the twelve megahertz marine band, l heard the following CW shore stations: GKB England, LPD Argentina, EAD Spain, TAH Turkey, HPP Panama, UGC The Ukraine, plus dozens of US and Canadian ship and shore stations. This while using my "Rock's Own Blooper" on a twelve-foot indoor antenna.

You can easily do as well, and even better. Toss-together a nice little regenerative receiver and find-out for yourself, it's cheap and easy.

I found a beautiful old two-tube ('57 detector and '56 audio amplifier) blooper up in my attic I had built and used with great joy back in the middle thirties. But, with tear in eye, I decided to desecrate it. It was built in one of those neat little 7x7 cubical metal cabinets and was full of all kinds of goodies: National variable condensers, an Isolantite coil socket, etc, etc. It also has one of those beautiful National Velvet Vernier dials on the front. The 500 henry plate choke, though had long since opened up and many other parts have become raunchy with age. So, I pulled out all the tube stuff and have built another "Rock's Own Blooper" using the same circuit in its cabinet instead. It works almost as well as the old tube job did as I recall. So maybe, I didn't desecrate it after all.

It may be of interest to recall that the original was built back in 1937, the year that the Hindenburg cracked up in New Jersey. This makes it 60 years old, and me 19 years old when I built it...

The original tube receiver was very similar to that described on pages 102-103.

I was very proud of this device, and still am.

Why JFETS over Bipolars?

You may wonder why I chose JFET type transistors rather than bipolar types that can deliver higher amplification. Bipolar transistors have a low input impedance on the order of a thousand ohms. Vacuum tubes have very high input impedances on the order of megohms. If we want to adapt old tube circuits to solid-state components, we need a JFET which also has a very high input impedance. Considerable circuit modifications must be made to get bipolar transistors to work properly as regenerative detectors. The simple plug-in coils described don't work very well. I have not been pleased with the results I obtained using bipolar transistors as regenerative detectors in traditional circuits. More experiments are needed though. Bipolar transistors make excellent audio amplifiers.

Superregeneration

You may wonder why I've said nothing so far about superregeneration. The superregenerative detector is extremely sensitive but it radiates a very strong and noisy signal while operating which can interfere with other receivers and electronic equipment. In addition, it is a broad band receiver which can be useful at very high frequencies (VHF) but makes it virtually useless in use in the high frequency (HF) spectrum in which we are interested. Many years ago, superregenerative receivers were popular with radio amateurs for use in the VHF amateur bands where there was at the time plenty of empty radio spectrum in which to wallow. But that was before the advent of television and other radio services which now crowd the VHF and UHF spectrum. Some of our old-time superregenerative receivers radiated almost as well as the transmitters of the era. Such radiation would be illegal now. Because of these technical difficulties, superregeneration has fallen by the wayside in today's electronic world, and is, at least in my opinion, is an obsolete technology that should not be resurrected.

Proper Regenerative Operation

To conclude lets talk about how to operate a regenerative receiver which might be almost as much of an art as building one.

There are three golden rules which must be kept firmly in mind here. The first is to always tune across a frequency band very slowly. Distant stations do not pop out at you the way they do with a modern superheterodyne receiver. You have to tune for them!

Second, when tuning for distant AM stations, such as shortwave broadcast stations, advance the regeneration control as close to the oscillation point as possible. This is where both the sensitivity and the selectivity is at its maximum.

Third, when tuning for a CW radiotelegraph signal, set the regeneration control just barely over the threshold but definitely into the oscillating region of operation. We'll talk about this setting in a moment. Also, when tuning for the single-sideband voice signals amateurs use, tune as you would for a CW station. In this case, however, you must carefully adjust both the tuning and the regeneration controls to clear what sounds like "duck quackings" into intelligible speech. Tuning in a single-sideband signal is a tricky procedure, and it will require quite a bit of practice before you acquire the knack. But keep trying! Figure 4.12 shows graphically just how the amount of regeneration affects the detector's sensitivity.

When tuning in a CW radiotelegraph signal, simply adjust the regeneration control to just beyond the oscillation point and tune in the signal until you have a beat note with a pitch you find easy to copy. For many people about 800 Hz is pleasant. You can approach zero beat from the high side by tuning from a higher to a lower frequency. Or you can approach zero beat from the low side by tuning upward in frequency. Either approach will give you the same pitch, but the background signals will slightly different because you are tuned to a slightly different frequency. Tune the signal in on the side of zero-beat at which you experience the least interference from other signals.

One obvious question from this is: why

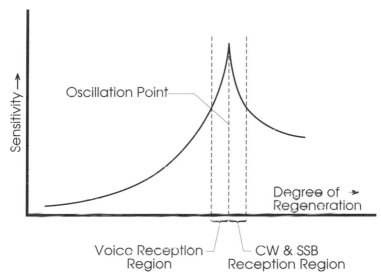

Figure 4.12 – *Careful Adjustment of Regeneration is Essential in Order to Achieve Maximum Sensitivity*

does the sensitivity of the detector drop off so rapidly after one passes the oscillation point? If you could connect a DC milliammeter in series with the plate power source, it would probably be easier to understand. As the oscillation grows stronger, the rectified DC grid voltage becomes more and more negative and, as a result, the smaller the DC plate current becomes. Plate current has dropped but plate voltage has stayed the same. Since power is the product of voltage and current, it should be apparent that the output power of the tube has dropped. The tube's ability to amplify has decreased. With a JFET, a similar interaction between increased negative gate voltage and drain current occurs.

Fringe Howl

Sometimes a most disturbing condition will develop in the performance of a regenerative detector which will almost entirely spoil the sensitivity of the circuit. As the regeneration control is brought up gradually toward that point at which the circuit just begins to oscillate, that most critical and most sensitive condition, it will not enter into oscillation with a smooth "tunk" sound. Instead, it goes into the oscillating condition with a disturbing sort of a "burrrrrp". This almost certainly prevents the circuit being set or retained at its state of greatest sensitivity. Among radio amateurs this is known as "fringe howl" because if always occurs at the fringe of oscillation. There has always seemed to be a mystery as to its cause. What makes it so mysterious is that it is difficult to predict. It occurs in some receivers but not in others, although their circuits might seem to be identical. Its cause was certainly not understood for a long time.

After many years, a theory explaining the cause of fringe howl has been developed which seems to explain it adequately enough to allow us to cure the problem. Fringe howl always seems to occur when one, or both, of two different conditions exist in the same circuit, namely, 1) there is an audio transformer between the detector and the first audio amplifier stage or, 2) the detector grid leak resistor is too small or the grid bypass capacitor is too small for optimum operation.

This theory has developed out of the observation that if a resistance coupling system – that is, a plate resistor, coupling capacitor and audio amplifier grid resistor combination – is used between detector and amplifier, fringe howl never occurs. This lends credence to the idea that what is happening during fringe howl is that just as the detector goes into oscillation, the DC detector plate current suddenly decreases. When the current drops fast enough, the magnetic field of the transformer begins to collapse the magnetic field inducing a brief voltage across the transformer primary. This causes the detector plate current to rise which in turn advances the circuit further into oscillation. But this advance toward oscillation causes plate current to again decrease, and the cycle starts all over again. If this rising and falling of plate current occurs at an audio frequency rate, from a couple hundred to a couple thousand hertz, it "sounds like a burp" as the regeneration control passes through its critical adjustment point. The exact frequency will be determined by values of the components used in the detector and in the coupling circuits between detector and audio amplifier stages.

Eliminating Fringe Howl

If your receiver uses an audio transformer between detector and first audio amplifier stage which is ordinarily a good design but it develops fringe howl, what can you do about it? First, try reducing the capacitance of the detector grid capacitor to around 50 picofarad, rather than the 100 - 250 pfd that we often see used. Then, increase the grid leak resistance to about ten megohms. Even 20 megohms has been successfully used. This has no negative effect upon detector sensitivity. In fact, a large grid leak resistor often increases sensitivity!

If these two fixes do not cure the burping, connect a high resistance across the secondary of the audio transformer, the higher the better. Try one megohm at first. If that doesn't fix it, reduce it to 500 kilohms, then 250 kilohms. You want a resistance small enough to cure the howl, but no smaller than necessary, since too low a value will reduce the available audio amplification. From experience, I have found that a value of less than 100 kilohms is seldom needed.

One other circuit condition that can contribute to fringe howl is coupling that is far too "tight" between tickler coil and the tuned coil feeding the detector grid. Try removing a turn or two from the tickler coil. Or try to increase the separation between the coils just a bit. This often helps.

Fringe Howl is a condition which should not be allowed to exist in any regenerative receiver. Fix it right away and be done with it!

Double Twin Triode Receiver

Let's consider a couple variations of regenerative receiver circuits. If you have a power supply which can convert 120 VAC into, say, 300 volts of well-filtered DC, you might try building the set shown in Figure 4-13.

This receiver was built and used effectively as part of a "semi-portable" amateur station at W9SCH. Two 6N7GT tubes were used. These are dual medium-mu triodes, once used extensively in military gear. There should yet be a number of these tubes to be found in ham shacks, hamfests, etc. The RF amplifier and detector share one tube, the two audio amplifiers the second. It produces surprisingly loud signals using a ten foot piece of wire for an antenna. All capacitors are in picofarads, mica or ceramic, unless otherwise stated. The "gimmick" is four or five turns of insulated hookup wire twisted together but not electrically connected to make an itty-bitty capacitor. All resistors are one watt carbon, unless otherwise stated. The tuning coil is tapped for the detector cathode to provide regeneration instead of using a tickler coil. This frequently seen cir-

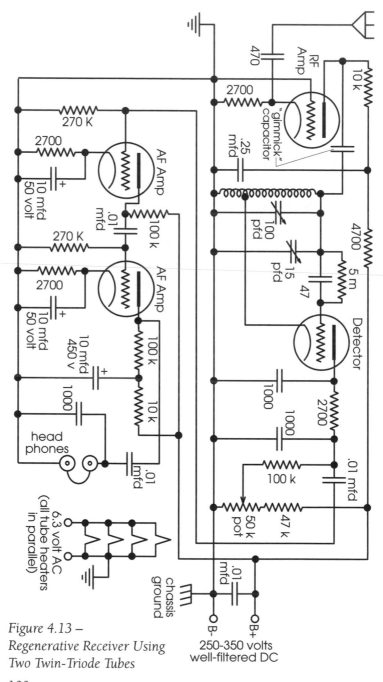

Figure 4.13 –
Regenerative Receiver Using
Two Twin-Triode Tubes

cuit is called the Hartley oscillator circuit.

In my version, a 100 pfd variable served as the band set capacitor. In parallel with it was a 15 pfd variable which was driven by the main tuning dial. This arrangement spread the amateur band out over a large part of the dial. This technique was common in receivers used in amateur radio. This receiver was built upon a large aluminum chassis which also held a two-stage, crystal-controlled transmitter for the 80 meter amateur band, as well as the DC power supply fed from 120 volt AC house current. With this little station, many interesting CW radiotelegraph contacts were made, from coast to coast and with Canada.

Please note that the headphones are isolated from the higher than normal voltage on the amplifier plate with a .01 mfd capacitor in the interest of safety. The RF amplifier between antenna and detector isolates the antenna from the detector. Antenna problems have less chance in disrupting the delicate adjustment of detector oscillation, and RF produced by an oscillating detector has less chance of being radiated accidentally by the antenna.

The tuning coil for the 80 meter band, 3.5 - 4.0 MHz, is 35 turns, close wound, with any reasonable size magnet wire, tapped for the cathode at three turns from the ground end.

Pentode-Triode Receiver

Figure 4.14 shows another good regenerative receiver circuit which I have used with great success.

If carefully built, this receiver is especially effective for long range reception when used with a dipole antenna. Normally it requires between 200 and 300 volts of well-filtered DC, and 6.3 volts AC from a line-operated power supply. The detector tube should be any of the once common RF metal case pentodes types 6SJ7, 6SK7, 6SH7, etc with the metal case grounded. The audio amplifier may be any of the medium-mu triodes, 6J5, 6C5, etc. either metal or glass. All capacitor values are in picofarads being ceramic or mica unless otherwise stated, and all resistors one-watt carbon. Be sure to ground the metal case of the detector tube. You may use a miniature equivalent tube if you like, but I prefer the larger size metal tubes, myself.

The 100 pfd variable capacitor is the bandset capacitor. Again, the bandset capacitor is adjusted to the edge of the amateur band, or other frequency range being listened to. The 15 pfd variable capacitor then spreads the signals out conveniently. As before, the bandspread capacitor should be driven by a quality vernier dial. This receiver would best be built upon a metal chassis and equipped with a metal panel. As with all regenerative receivers *solid construction is mandatory!* The

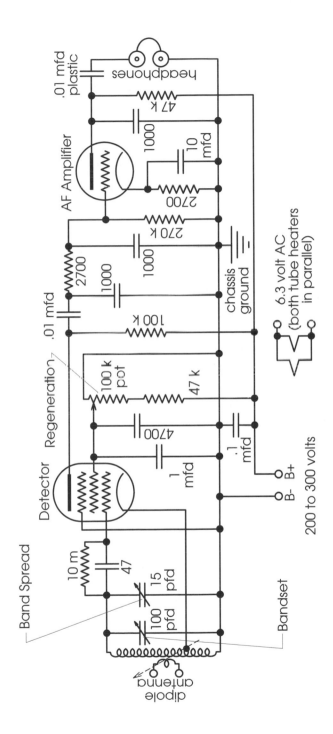

Figure 4.14 – Pentode - Triode Regenerative Receiver

103

plug-in coils recommended are wound upon 1 1/4 inch diameter plastic forms, such as the tube-base forms as previously discussed, close wound with any reasonable magnet wire. The antenna coupling coil is a single turn of No 14 B&S, mounted independently and concentrically with the plug-in coil being used. Some suggested coil data is tabulated in Figure 4.15.

Wave Length	No. Turns	Cathode Tap (turns from ground end)
20 Meters	5	1
40 Meters	15	2
80 Meters	35	3

Figure 4-15 –
Coil Data for Pentode-Triode Receiver

If this receiver is carefully built, intelligently operated and radio conditions are at all good, you should be able to receive the weakest amateur as well as the strong commercial stations from anywhere on this planet, wherever a radio signal path exits between that station's antenna and yours. (and if interference permits…)

The Double Regenerative Superhet

The double regenerative superheterodyne is an extremely challenging project which should not be attempted by anyone lacking considerable experience in both receiver construction and operation (Fig. 4.16). But for those able to build and operate it correctly, it is a very sensitive and relatively highly selective receiver worth having. Its performance compares well with receivers containing several more tubes or transistors and costing much more.

Being a superheterodyne, it operates upon the beat frequency principle. A signal is generated within the receiver by an oscillator circuit, tube V3. This signal is combined in the mixer circuit, tube V1, to produce by heterodyning, another radio frequency signal whose frequency is the difference between the oscillator signal and that signal coming in through the antenna. This difference frequency signal is then coupled into the detector tube V2. The detector then operates as would any other regenerative detector. However, this detector remains tuned to a fixed frequency which, being lower than the signal frequency, can be more stable than one working at the input or received signal frequency, and can produce more gain.

In operation, the mixer is tuned to the desired signal frequency. The regenerative control is set just below the oscillation point,

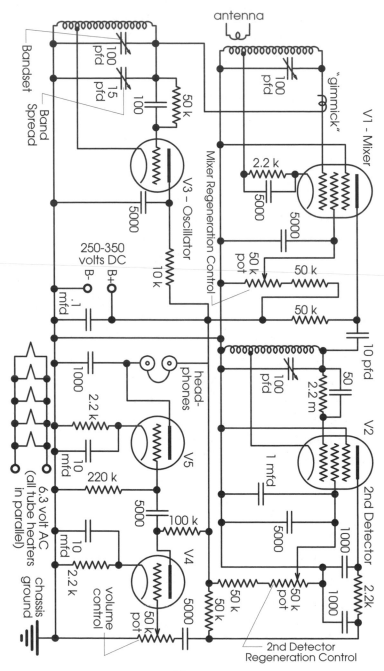

Figure 4.16 – Double Regenerative Receiver

making the detector very sensitive and selective enough to keep out much interference and noise. The oscillator circuit must be carefully tuned to a frequency sufficiently higher such that the difference between the incoming signal frequency and the mixer frequency is identical to that of the second detector. It is the oscillator circuit which must be set up for bandspread tuning with a slow motion vernier dial.

I built and used this type of receiver in connection with an amateur CW telegraph transmitter in a transceiver circuit. Operation was in the 21 megaHertz, 15-meter amateur band. Many long range amateur contacts with all continents and many foreign countries were made.

The second detector circuit was rigidly tuned to a frequency of 8.5 megahertz. Choosing the proper operating frequency for the detector is a cardinal problem with this type of receiver. The detector frequency must not be an integral sub-multiple of either the received signal nor of the oscillator frequency, or these will interfer with one another, and the receiver won't operate.

A frequency must also be chosen which is not used by a powerful commercial station. Even with carefully shielded circuits, enough of such signals can leak through to cause interference which cannot be tuned out. My choice of 8.5 megaHertz, satisfactory when my receiver was built two decades ago, is now the home of many new stations. I'm at a loss to suggest a useable second detector frequency. There are too many different factors involved. For this and other reasons, this particular circuit design is offered primarily to illustrate an interesting application of the regenerative design rather than as a suggested project. Its time may have come and gone which is to be expected in these rapidly changing times. Nevertheless, trying one of these circuits will teach you a great deal.

Tube Pin Connections

You may ask about pin connections upon the tube sockets? Which pin connects to what in the circuit? The days in which an author could prescribe complete construction data for a piece of apparatus, and the reader could go to any good radio parts supplier and obtain the components over the counter are now past. All I can do is to state the basic requirements of any tube or part and suggest some alternatives which may work. For example, in our discussion I suggested that any medium-mu triode or any RF pentode will serve in a particular application. But I have no way of knowing exactly what tube you might be able to locate. Different tubes, of the same class and function, have widely varying pin connections. So, what then? The most practical suggestion I can make is to refer you to any issue of the *The Radio Amateur's Handbook* published by the AMERICAN RADIO RELAY LEAGUE before 1978. The last issue of the handbook to contain anything like complete tube data was the 1977 edition. In an appendix of this handbook and most editions in the years before it is a complete listing of all common American vacuum tubes in use at the date of issue including base connection diagrams.

All American tube manufacturers published manuals describing in detail the properties of their tubes. The Radio Corporation of America's (RCA) tube manual apparently had the widest distribution of all such manuals, and as a result should be the easiest to find today in used bookstores, libraries, and at hamfests. Some tube manuals are even being reprinted. Many amateurs, especially older radio experimenters, are likely to yet have copies of these books or their equivalents upon their bookshelves. Well-stocked public libraries in the larger cities may also have copies as well as the libraries of colleges, universities or possibly even larger high schools.

Older Books Hold Secrets

In addition to tube information, the older handbooks also contain much helpful information relevant to regenerative receiver construction which may be interesting and helpful to you. But, as much as it may disturb us, the truth is, the construction of regenerative receivers is an art and a science of the past. Packet radio, the Internet and complex technology seem to be the rage. With the excitement these media offer, few people are interested in exploring the incredible receiver performance possible with unbelievable simplicity. This is a tough nut to crack, but it is life, and we must accept it, like it or not.

The home construction of scientific and technical apparatus is a venerable activity that has inspired creative individuals for centuries. Your work in building, troubleshooting and using simple but effective radio receivers makes you a true follower in this tradition. As with those before you, your work trains your hands, expands your mind and stimulates your imagination, regardless of the simplicity of what you build. Do not allow anyone, preaching mere modernity talk you out of it. Hang in there, have fun, and good luck!

Part Five

Sample Regenerative
Receiver Circuits

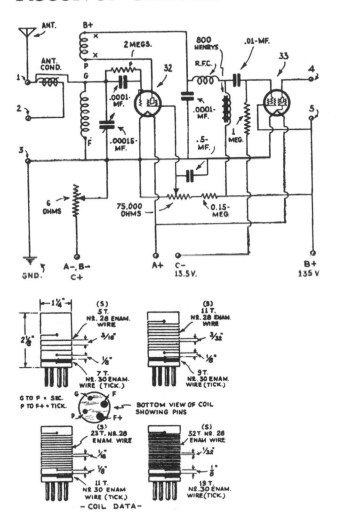

Federated "Air Rover"
from 1934 OFFICIAL SHORTWAVE RADIO MANUAL

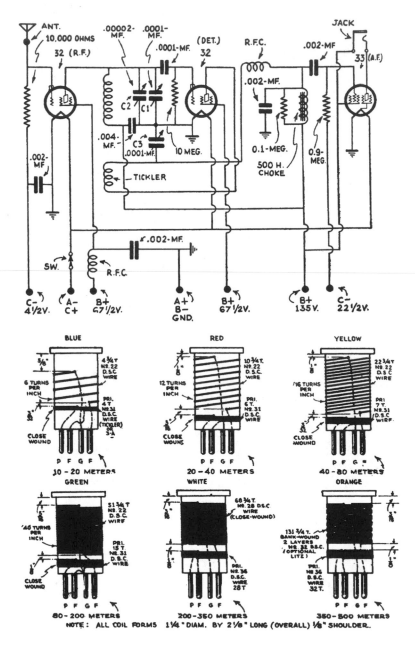

Gross "Eagle Band-Spread Set"
from 1934 OFFICIAL SHORTWAVE RADIO MANUAL

112

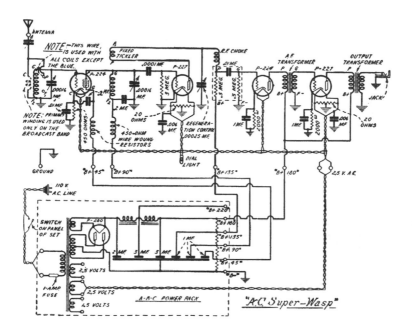

Pilot "A.C. Super-Wasp"
from 1934 OFFICIAL SHORTWAVE RADIO MANUAL

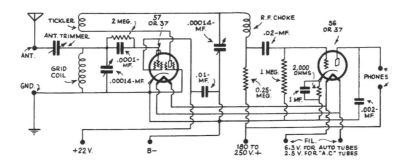

Radio Trading Company "Electrified Doerle 2 Tube AC Receiver"
from 1934 OFFICIAL SHORTWAVE RADIO MANUAL

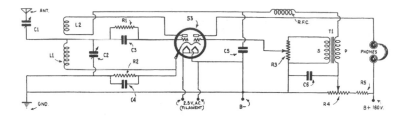

The "53" 1-Tube Twinplex
from 1934 OFFICIAL SHORTWAVE RADIO MANUAL

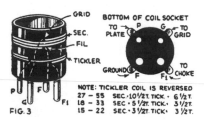

(left)
2-Tube "Old Reliable"
from 1934 OFFICIAL
SHORTWAVE RADIO
MANUAL

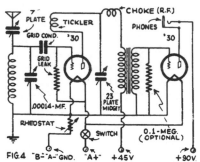

Details for building Mr. Simmons' 2-Tube Short-Wave Receiver, including wiring diagram.

(below)
The Famous Doerle "2-Tuber" Adapted to A.C. Operation
from 1934 OFFICIAL SHORTWAVE RADIO MANUAL

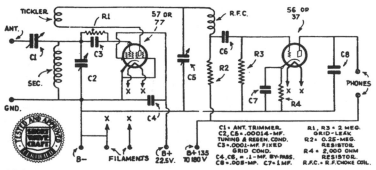

114

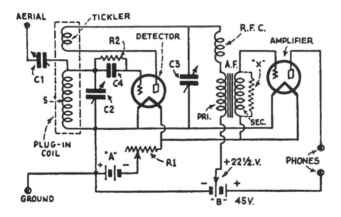

Approximate Wavelength (meters)	Sec.	Tickler
14- 25	4	6
23- 41	7	9
40- 85	14	12
83-125	23	23
120-200	36	36

Building the 2-Tube "Globe Trotter" from 1934 OFFICIAL SHORTWAVE RADIO MANUAL

A 2-Tube Receiver that Reaches the 12,500 Mile Mark from 1934 OFFICIAL SHORTWAVE RADIO MANUAL

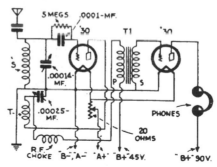

1—Bakelite panel 7"x10" ;
1—Baseboard 9x11" ;
3—UX Sockets;
1—Tuning Condenser .00014-mf.
1—Throttle Condenser .00025-mf. ;
2—Condenser Plates 1½" square ;
7—Terminal Post-strip ;
7—Binding Posts ;
5—Megohm Grid-leak ;
1—.0001-mf. Grid Condenser ;
1—5 :1 Transformer ;
2—Telephone Binding Posts ;
2—3" Dials ;
1—20-Ohm Rheostat ;
Hook-up wire, screws, etc.

COIL DATA

Range (meters)	Turns S	T
15-45	5	6
35-75	9	5
60-125	16	6

All coils are close-wound with No. 24 enamelled copper wire, and with no spacing between S and T.

115

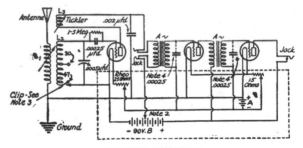

CIRCUIT DIAGRAM

L1—Antenna coil 20 turns 2¾" dia. No. 22 wire. Wound spaced or solid layer.
Notes—1.—Wavelength range 190-450 using 30 turns, on up to 575 using 47 turns.
2.—Detector voltage variable 16-37.
3.—Turns variable by clip inside set, not by switch or panel.
4.—250 uufd (.0025 microfarad) shunt condensers used only if set insists on whistling.

QST March 1926
A Modern Regenerative Receiver
by Felix Anderson

QST Magazine October 1926 featuring "An All Wave Receiver"

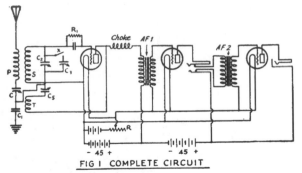

FIG I COMPLETE CIRCUIT

QST October 1926
Receiver for 15 to18,000 meter wavelengths
C – 1500 mmfd (with very long antenna)
C1– 1 mfd
C2– 125 mmfd
C3– 125 mmfd
C4– 150 mmfd
C5– 500 mmfd
grid leak– 50 mmfd & 5 to10 megohms
R– 6 ohm wirewound

QST October 1926 – Fig 4 Top View. Note Terminal Strip for Plug-In Coils

QST October 1926 – Fig 3 Rear View of Receiver with Long Wave Coils

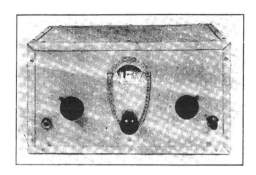

QST October 1929 – A "1929" Receiver by Paul S. Hendricks

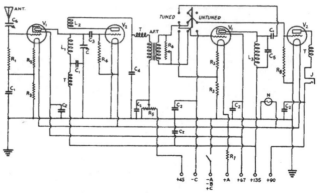

FIGURE 1

R1—50,000 ohms. "Grid-leak type resistor" or r.f.c. (See text).
R2—10 ohms. Fixed resistor.
R3—5 ohms. Fixed resistor.
R4—8 meghoms.
R5—100,000 ohm Frost variable resistor.
R6—200,000 ohm Frost variable resistor.
R7—¾-amp. Amperite.
R8—2 meghoms.
C—Pilot Midget variable condensers (see photos and text).
C1—0.006 μfd. Sangamo fixed condenser.
C2—1.0 μfd. Sangamo by-pass condensers.
C3—0.0001 μfd. Sangamo fixed condenser.
C4—0.001 μfd. Sangamo fixed condenser.
C5—0.01 μfd. Aerovox fixed condenser.
C6—0.00005 μfd. (50μμfd.) Pilot midget variable condenser.
L1—Plug-in inductances (see text).
L2—Tickler.
L3—Secondary of Ford spark coil.
T—R.f. chokes. Silver-Marshall, type No. 275.
AFT—Audio frequency transformer, Sangamo high quality type.
V1—CX-322.
V2—CX-301-A.
N—Dial lamp, as furnished on National drum dial.
J—Output Jack, single open circuit type.
G—To ground and metal cabinet.

			Tuning	Frequency Range in kc.	
Coil	Secondary	Tickler	Condenser	Max.	Min.
No. 1	2 turns	3 turns	5 plates	30,000	27,770
No. 2	8 "	5 "	2 "	14,635	13,955
No. 3	19 "	6 "	2 "	7,370	6,895
No. 4	33 "	7 "	7 "	4,286	3,333
No. 5	8 "	4 "	23 "	14,285	8,820
No. 6	13 "	6 "	13 "	9,835	6,895
No. 7	20 "	7 "	23 "	7,060	4,286

COIL AND CONDENSER COMBINATION

QST October 1929 – A "1929" Receiver by Paul S. Hendricks

120

APPENDIX

In practical radio work we very seldom need to figure things precisely but the ability to make useful ballpark estimates is priceless. Here is some information which may help you use this most helpful estimating skill and build successful radio projects.

Length Units
One meter is about three feet.
One centimeter is about one-third inch.
There are about 25 millimeters in one inch.

Capacitance Units
The basic unit is the farad– important in theory but much too big for practical radio work. Our largest capacitors are measured in microfarad or millionths of a farad. Smaller capacitors are coming to be measured in nanofarads or thousands of picofarads. The smallest capacitors come in picofarads (formerly called micro-microfarads or somtimes "mikey-mikes") or millionths of a microfarad.

Inductance Units
The basic unit here is the henry, often seen in the low-frequency components used in power supplies and audio frequency amplifiers. The millihenry, less often used, but equal to one-thousandth of the henry is found describing the inductance of radio frequency choke coils.

The microhenry, one-millionth of a henry, is the common unit in which radio tuning coils are measured.

Wavelengths

One wavelength, the important unit where antennas or transmission lines are involved, is the distance a radio wave travels during the time it takes an alternating current to complete one cycle. The more cycles crammed into one second, the quicker it takes to complete each cycle. The resulting wavelength is shorter. Wavelengths are usually measured in meters throughout the world. For our general convenience, we may approximately say that the wavelengths of the AM broadcast band center around 300 meters, or about one thousand feet.

The so-called "short waves", probably of greatest importance to us, extend from about 100 meters or 300 feet to about ten meters or 30 feet.

The FM broadcast band wavelengths center around three meters or ten feet.

Present day (1995) low band VHF-TV wavelengths center around four meters, or about twelve feet. UHF-TV wavelengths are about one-half meter or about 1 1/2 feet in length.

Relationship Between
Wavelength and Frequency
To speak of the speed of light or of radio wave travel as 186,300 miles per second is precise but inconvenient. It seems easier to think of this speed as 300 meters per microsecond. If we do this, we may easily relate wavelength and frequency with a simple equation.

$$\text{wavelength in meters} = \frac{300}{\text{frequency in mHz}}$$

– or –

$$\text{megaHertz} = \frac{300}{\text{wavelength in meters}}$$

Estimating Tuned Circuit
Component Sizes Easily
One may use the classical equation for calculating these but this algebraic effort is not necessary. Instead, we may use what are called "LC Products" or oscillation constants, which make this so much easier. Given below are the oscillation constants for a number of frequencies of possible interest in our work.

To use these, simply divide the oscillation constant given in the table by, for instance, the capacitance of your tuning capacitor in picofarads, to find the inductance in microhenrys of the coil you need to tune to that frequency. Or divide the appropriate oscillation constant by the coil's inductance, in microhenrys to find the right capacitance in picofarads to tune it.

Amateur Band (wavelength)	Oscillation Constant
80 meters	2070
40 meters	517
30 meters	248
20 meters	129

Oscillation Constants

Frequency in megaHertz	Oscillation Constant
30	28.1
20	63.3
15	112
10	253
7.5	450
5	1013
3	2814
1	25300

No fuss, muss, or cuss! You don't even need a square root.

To find an oscillation-constant for any frequency not given above, simply divide the number 25330 by the square of the frequency in megahertz. The result my then be used as above.

Calculating Coil Dimensions

This simple but useful formula can help you estimate the number of turns needed on cylindri-

$$N = \sqrt{\frac{L \times \left(1 + \frac{D}{2.3}\right)}{0.05 \times D^2}}$$

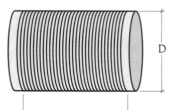

N = number of turns required (drop any fraction of a turn, round off to whole turns)

L = coil inductance in microhenries

D = coil diameter in inches

l = width of winding on the form (distance between the first and last turn) in inches

124

cal form in order to achieve a desired inductance.

I use the formula myself and find it easier to use than most. The calculated values is as precise as coils can be wound by hand. If you like mathematics, try your hand at this.

Additional Coil Winding Data

Here is some additional coil-winding data that applies to 1-1/4 inch diameter tube base forms, close wound with No. 24, B&S enameled wire.

Number of Turns	Inductance (microhenries)	Resonant Freq (mHz) with 60 pfd cap
2	0.27	39
3	0.59	27
4	1.0	21
5	1.5	16
7	2.7	12
10	5.1	9.1
20	16	5.1
30	29	3.8

In as much as the effective inductance of any tuning coil is notably influenced by the tightness of winding, the length of the leads connecting it to its circuit, and its surroundings including the effect of the tickler coil, this data must be regarded as approximate only.

For use in most of the receiving circuits

described, the following winding data is suggested:

Coil No.	Turns Tuned Winding	Turns Tickler	Amateur Band approx. coverage
1	7	3	20 meters
2	15	4	40 meters
3	35	7	80 meters

Tickler coil is assumed to be spaced about 1/16 inch distant from the tuned winding.

It is understood that, when the typical 100 pfd maximum tuning capacitor is used, not only the designated amateur bands will be received, but also marine shore stations, shipboard stations other miscellaneous radio services, and lots of short-wave broadcast stations, both domestic and foreign.

Tube Types

Some suggested tube types that may be well used in good, homebuilt regenerative receivers. When visiting a thrift store or an amateur radio flea market, keep your eyes open for them:

Triodes for battery operation:
    1G4G, '30, '01-A, '99.
Triodes for AC power supply operation:
    6J5, 6C5, 56, 37.
RF Amplifier Pentodes:
    6SK7, 6SJ7, 6SH7, 6K7, 6J7.

Note: Never mind that "G" following a tube type number. This only refers to the glass bulb version of an otherwise metal tube. The electrical characteristics of G and non-G types are identical. In most cases the non-G, metal ones are preferred since the metal case may be grounded to reduce undesired circuit interaction and hum pickup. Both versions will usually work in any of the circuit described in this book.

General Comment Upon Required Precision in Practical Radio Work

In amateur circles, the components often used do not have values which are precisely known. Likewise the exact parameters of tubes or transistors are not usually available to us. Furthermore, there are a number of stray properties of any electronic circuit for which we often cannot account. So, while sloppiness is not condoned, fussiness is out of place. Therefore, it scarcely pays to be concerned about the values of the resistors and capacitors used more closely than plus or minus twenty percent of a value specified in a schematic diagram or parts list. Deviations of this magnitude very seldom have any observable effect upon circuit performance. "Be as precise as it pays to be, but no more so" is the rule best kept in mind in practical radio. Concentrate your effort in careful construction work where it does pay off.

1 GY 30 OIA 99